NUFFIELD
NATIONAL CURRICULUM
MATHEMATIC

Handling data 3

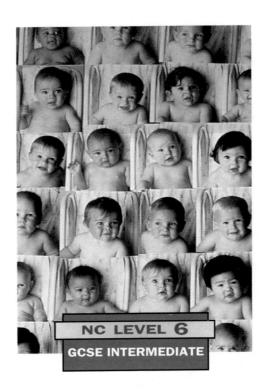

NC LEVEL 6

GCSE INTERMEDIATE

Heinemann

Project director: Peter Reynolds
Assistant director: Mike Cornelius
Project manager: Jan Hoare

Author of this book
Jean Wilson with additional material by David Cassell
Edited by Peter Reynolds

Heinemann Educational
a division of Heinemann Publishers (Oxford) Ltd,
Halley Court, Jordan Hill, Oxford, OX2 8EJ

OXFORD   LONDON   EDINBURGH
MADRID   ATHENS   BOLOGNA   PARIS
MELBOURNE   SYDNEY   AUCKLAND   SINGAPORE   TOKYO
IBADAN   NAIROBI   HARARE   GABORONE
PORTSMOUTH NH (USA)

First published 1995

95 96 97 98
10 9 8 7 6 5 4 3 2 1

ISBN 0 435 50551 3

Designed and typeset by Ken Vail Graphic Design
Illustrated by Ann Baum, Rupert Besley, Joan Corlass, Brian Hoskin, Hussein Hussein, Sue King,
Mike Lacey, Nigel Paige, Graeme Morris (Ken Vail Graphic Design)
Printed in Spain by Mateu Cromo, S.A. Pinto (Madrid)

Acknowledgements
The project and publishers gratefully acknowledge the contribution made by the late Hilary Shuard.
The authors and publishers would like to thank for permission to reproduce the following
photographs and copyright material:
p.1 Michael Holford; p.1 E.T. Archive/Public Record Office; p.2 Mary Evans Picture Library; p.88
Hutchinson Library
Cover image: ACE Photo Agency
HMSO for permission to reproduce the National Curriculum level descriptions.

Every effort has been made to contact copyright holders of material published in this book.
Any omissions will be rectified in subsequent printings if notice is given to the publisher.

> **Cover picture**
> All these babies look different. You could record their different characteristics such
> as eye colour and weight in a survey. There is more about surveys in Unit 1.

About this book

This book is part of the Nuffield National Curriculum Mathematics series. It will help you learn mathematics and we hope you will enjoy using it.

How this book is organized

There are nine units of work in this book. They are numbered Unit 1 to Unit 9. Each unit provides information for you to read and questions and activities for you to do.

The units are presented in short sections. Each section has a letter and a title. For example, Section B of Unit 2 has the title:

B Stocking the cinema kiosk

The questions and activities in Section B are numbered **B1**, **B2**, **B3** and so on to help you find them easily

The contents list on the next page shows you where each unit and section starts and tells you what mathematics they cover.

Symbols used in the Nuffield books

These symbols are shown in the margin of your book whenever you need worksheets, equipment or access to a computer:

this means you need Worksheet H3:4 from the Assessment and Resource Pack.

you need equipment listed between the lines.

you need access to a computer and the software shown.

Contents

UNIT 1   *We need to know the facts!*

A The Census

A survey of the resources of England in lands, goods and people was commissioned in 1086 by William the Conqueror so that he could assess exactly what he had won at the Battle of Hastings.

The survey became known as the Domesday Book. It was never intended as a count of the population, but as a tallying of property and land. It is the earliest recorded survey of its kind.

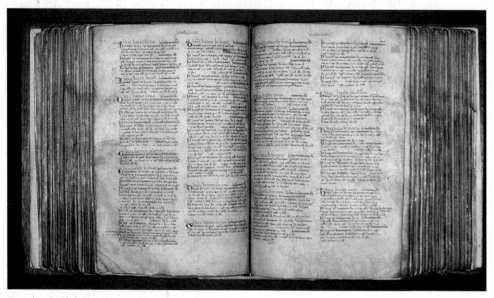

In the Middle Ages the clergy started to keep registers of the births, deaths and marriages in each parish.

By the eighteenth century, various states and countries started to undertake counts of population or **censuses**.

The job of taking the census was given to the clergy and 'overseers of the poor' or other 'substantial householders'.

The clergy had to provide information on the number of baptisms and burials for each ten year period from 1700 to 1780 and each year since. Marriages were to be recorded for every year since 1754.

'Overseers of the poor' and 'substantial householders' were given the job of recording the number of inhabited houses and the number of males and females living within the limits of their parish. They also had to record the number of persons chiefly employed in agriculture, trade, manufacture or handicraft.

It was not until 1800 that the first Census Act was passed in Britain for the purpose of '... taking account of the population of Great Britain ... .' It was a time of many wars and the government needed to find out how many people were employed on the land and were able to produce food. It also wanted to know how many people needed feeding.

From 1841, the **General Register Office** in London became responsible for censuses and the modern system came into existence.

The whole country was divided into districts, each of which had a registrar who was responsible for the collection and recording of information in their district.

Each registrar subdivided his district into areas containing no more than 200 inhabited houses. **Enumerators** were then appointed to collect information in each area using a standardized form.

The enumerators had to visit each household, explaining how to fill in the form which was then left behind to be completed on Census Day. The next day, the enumerator collected the form and made sure that each part was filled in correctly because at that time many people could neither read nor write.

The information asked for on the Census form was name, marital status, relationship with the head of the household, age, sex, 'rank, profession or occupation', parish and county of birth and description of medical disabilities.

So, in 1801, the first official count of the people in Britain took place. The Census has been taken every ten years since 1801 except 1941 (due to the Second World War).

The information needed by the government changes with time. Nowadays, 'type of dwelling' and 'ethnic origin' have been added to the form.

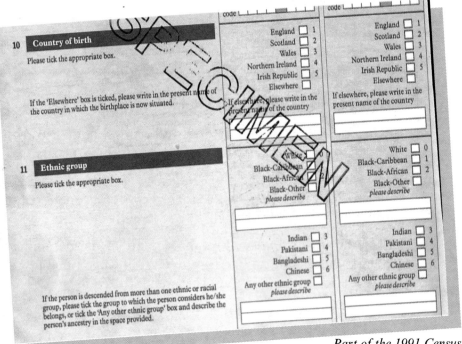

Part of the 1991 Census

Now answer these questions.

A1   What was the reason for compiling the Domesday Book?

A2   Throughout history, who were the main keepers of information about local people?

A3   Which year was the first official government count of the people of Britain taken?

A4   Why was it needed?

A5   When was the last Census taken?

A6   What use might a modern government make of the information?

B Opinion polls

In 1936, Dr George Gallup predicted the victory of Franklin D. Roosevelt in that year's American Election for President. He was able to do it from an opinion poll of the voting intentions of only 2000 people.

These 2000 people were selected as being a **representative sample** of the entire population of the USA in respect of their age, sex, social class and geographical spread.

Professional **pollsters** have to keep detailed data on the population of the country. For example, if they know that 20% of the population is over 65, then 20% of their sample must be over 65. If 54% of the population is male, then the sample must be 54% male.

Collecting opinions is a growing business as more and more groups, such as large companies, politicians and the news media seek information on how people might vote or what they think.

Spain still holiday-makers' choice according to new opinion poll

POLLS SAY OUR FAVOURITE FOOD IS CHOCOLATE

Latest poll gives Government a 2% lead

Radio 1 is tops says BBC poll

Cats are best pets say pollsters

Opinion polls can be taken either by **researchers** conducting interviews in the street, by people filling in coupons in newspapers and magazines, or by people answering 'phone-ins'.

Researchers have to be very careful not to influence the results of their polls – or **bias** them – by the way they carry them out. Interviews in the street can be biased. The results of a survey using newspaper coupons or by 'phone-in' may also produce bias, as only those with a strong view will take the trouble to cut out and post the coupon or to telephone.

Commercial organizations often hire professional pollsters to carry out opinion polls to find out how their products are doing, or how effective their latest advertising campaign has been.

The *method* of conducting the poll can affect the results. For example, telephone polling is becoming more popular but not everyone in Britain has a telephone, so any poll conducted wholly by telephone may provide biased results.

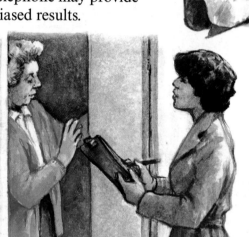

The *timing* of the poll may also be crucial as specific groups of people are never at home at particular times of the day. For example, office workers are unlikely to be at home between the usual office hours of 9 a.m. and 5 p.m.

The *place* of the interview is also important. For example, a survey conducted outside a railway station may catch mainly people who travel to work by train every day, whereas one carried out in a shopping centre on a week-day will catch a variety of people but these will be mainly shoppers. These two groups will probably have very different ideas on some matters, such as opening shops on Sundays.

The results of opinion polls are only as good as the questions asked and the choice of people asked to respond to them. One difficulty is that the more care that is taken in preparing the questions, the more expensive the research becomes. More care in selecting the people for interview also increases the cost of the poll.

As soon as a poll is published it is out of date, as the results of a poll may change the views of those who contributed to it.
For example, people who were not concerned about a local housing development, because they thought it would never happen, may think differently when they see the results of a poll which shows that the project has general support.

Here are some questions for you to answer or to use in discussion.

B1 The Gallup Poll company has now been joined by many more companies who carry out polls. Find details of as many polling companies as you can from newspapers and television programmes. You may find information in your school's library or database.

B2 How can polling companies ensure that the poll they carry out is as accurate as possible?

B3 List the factors which control how most polls are carried out.

C Polls and surveys

Polls and surveys are often reported in newspapers. Their chief impact is made by the headlines or the diagrams and charts which accompany them. Few people read the whole article to check the details.

Geographers often use **radial charts** like the following to make a comparison between two places where people might live.

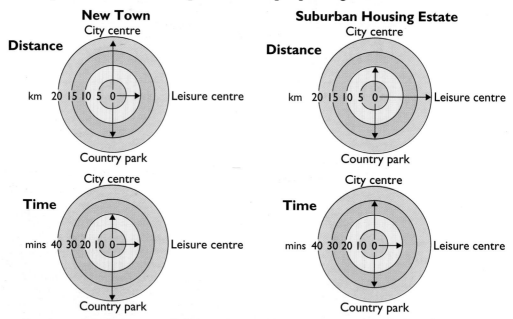

Look at the charts carefully and use them to copy and complete the following sentences.

C1   **a**   The inner circle of the top diagram for the New Town represents a distance of _____ from the centre of the town.

       b   The outer circle represents _____ .

       c   On the lower diagrams, the inner circle represents _____ and the outer one _____ .

Make sure that you understand the charts and then answer these questions.

C2   Do the inhabitants of the New Town or those of the Suburban Housing Estate have further to go to work in the city?

C3   Which set of people spend longer getting to work in the city?

C4   Compare the distances and travelling times to the leisure centre and the country park for both groups of people.

C5 All the following charts contain information. For each chart, write a short paragraph explaining the information illustrated.

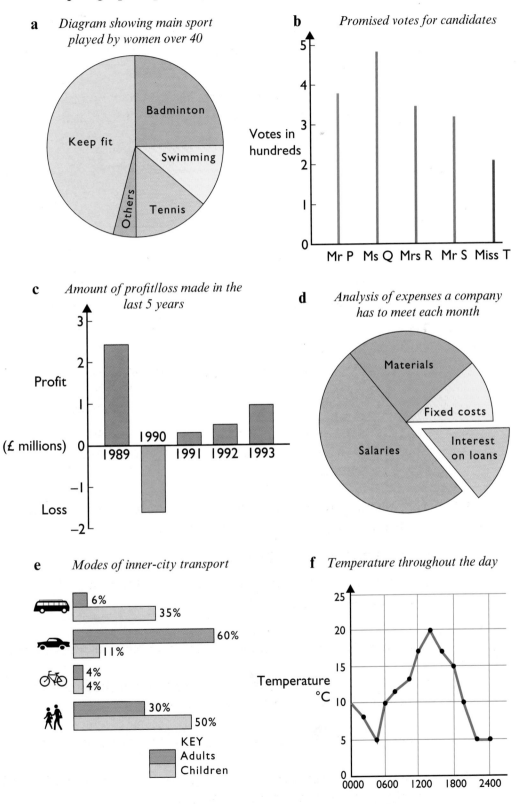

a *Diagram showing main sport played by women over 40*

Keep fit

Badminton

Swimming

Others

Tennis

b *Promised votes for candidates*

Votes in hundreds

Mr P   Ms Q   Mrs R   Mr S   Miss T

c *Amount of profit/loss made in the last 5 years*

Profit

(£ millions)

Loss

1989   1990   1991   1992   1993

d *Analysis of expenses a company has to meet each month*

Materials

Fixed costs

Interest on loans

Salaries

e *Modes of inner-city transport*

6%
35%

60%
11%

4%
4%

30%
50%

KEY
Adults
Children

f *Temperature throughout the day*

Temperature °C

0000   0600   1200   1800   2400

C6   Write a short paragraph commenting on these two charts, sometimes known as **population pyramids**, which show a comparison of the age groups living in the villages and new towns of Oldshire.

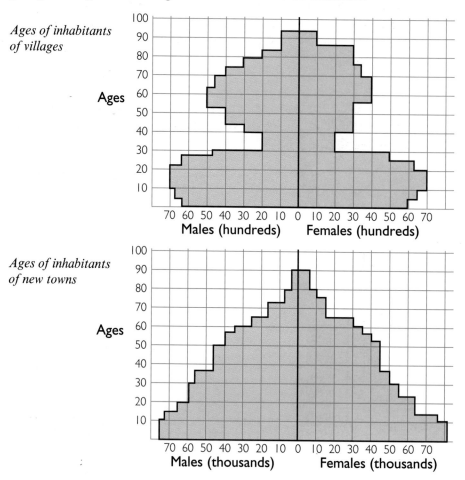

Ages of inhabitants of villages

Ages of inhabitants of new towns

C7   Here are two reports. Draw a chart to accompany each report.

a   The New Fish Fisheries Company reports profits in 1993 of £23 000 after making losses of £15 000 and £2000 in the previous two years. The management, disappointed at not making a profit in 1992, are convinced that it is increased efficiency that has achieved the turnaround in their fortunes since the loss of £15 000 in 1991.

b   The New Fish Fisheries Company have issued the following figures for catches of herring and cod for the last six months:

Fish caught in tonnes	Jul	Aug	Sept	Oct	Nov	Dec
Herring	21	20.5	25	27	33	35
Cod	12	17	9	15	14	10

C8 Illustrate the following survey result.

> Thirty per cent of the inhabitants of Bellview would like a by-pass road to be built to the north of the village. Fifteen per cent would prefer it to go to the south. Forty per cent would prefer no by-pass as they think it would reduce trade in the village, while others had no firm opinion.

C9 It is common to see misleading diagrams and headlines. Here are some for you to criticize. Describe why you think each of the following is misleading.

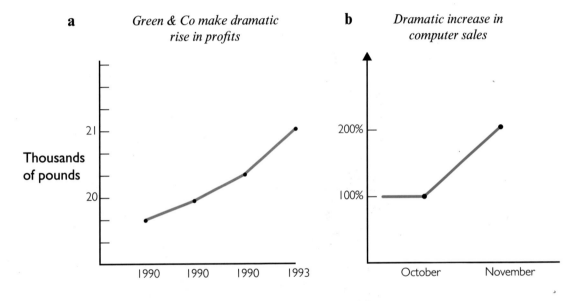

a   *Green & Co make dramatic rise in profits*

b   *Dramatic increase in computer sales*

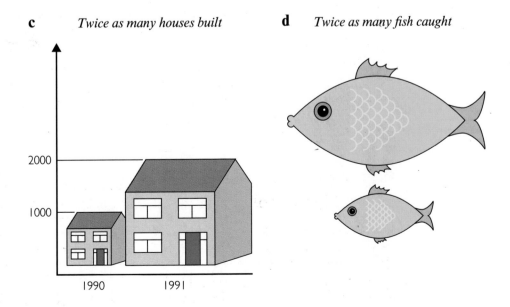

c   *Twice as many houses built*

d   *Twice as many fish caught*

UNIT 2 *Getting the right sample*

A Collecting information

To get worthwhile results, the collecting of responses to a questionnaire needs to be done with care.

You usually cannot ask everyone in a group to answer your questionnaire. You need to ask a selection of people – a **sample**.

However, this sample must mimic the characteristics or opinions of *all* the people in the group.

A1 Which of the groups **A**, **B** or **C** below best mimics this large group of people?

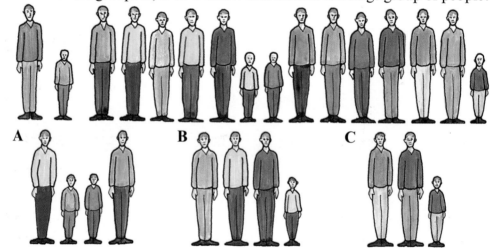

A2 Which of the groups **A**, **B** or **C** below best mimics this large group?

B Stocking the cinema kiosk

The management of a new cinema need to know what quantity of each type of refreshment to stock in the foyer kiosk.

They have decided to carry out a survey to find out what each member of the audience prefers.

As the cinema holds 300 people, a group of 30 will be chosen as a sample to mimic the buying habits of the larger group.

B1 Using the information about one specific cinema on the next two pages, choose 30 people by selecting every tenth person. (The seats have been numbered for you in bold.)

10		**20**		**30**
C		A		A
F		F		M
coke		ice		ice

    10th   20th   30th
    person   person   person

Code used here and on pages 13 and 14

C = under 16
Y = 16-24
A = 25-65
OAP = over 65

M = Male
F = Female

pop = popcorn
ice = ice cream
loll = lolly
choc = choc bar
coke = coke
oth = other drink

Record on a tally chart the refreshment chosen by each person.

Type	Tally	Total
Popcorn		
Ice cream	//	
Lolly		
Choc bar		
Coke	/	
Other drink		

B2 Using your tally chart, advise the cinema management on the quantities of stock they should put in the kiosk. Remember to cater for 300 people.

B3 Repeat the exercise using the 1st, 11th, 21st, etc. person.

B4 Are the results the same? Comment on any differences you find.

		300 Y M pop	299 Y M pop	298 Y M coke	297 A M coke	296 A F coke	295 A F coke	294 A M coke		
265 Y F coke	266 Y F coke	267 Y F coke	268 Y F pop	269 A M pop	270 A M pop	271 A M pop	272 A F pop	273 A F pop	274 A M pop	275 A M pop
264 A F ice	263 A F ice	262 A M ice	261 A F coke	260 A F coke	259 Y M coke	258 Y M pop	257 Y M coke	256 Y F pop	255 Y F pop	254 A F pop
221 A F pop	222 A F pop	223 A M pop	224 A F pop	225 Y M pop	226 A F oth	227 A F choc	228 A F choc	229 A M choc	230 A F coke	231 A M coke
220 A F pop	219 A F pop	218 Y M choc	217 Y M choc	216 Y M choc	215 A F coke	214 Y F pop	213 Y F pop	212 A M pop	211 A M coke	210 A M choc
177 A F ice	178 A F ice	179 OAP F choc	180 C M choc	181 C M choc	182 A M pop	183 C F loll	184 C M oth	185 OAP F ice	186 OAP F oth	187 OAP F oth
176 Y M pop	175 Y F coke	174 A M	173 OAP F choc	172 OAP F choc	171 A M choc	170 A F choc	169 Y F pop	168 Y F coke	167 C F choc	166 C M choc
133 Y M coke	134 Y M coke	135 Y F coke	136 A F coke	137 C M oth	138 C M oth	139 C F choc	140 C F loll	141 OAP F coke	142 OAP M coke	143 A F pop
132 Y F choc	131 Y F oth	130 Y F coke	129 C M oth	128 C M loll	127 A M ice	126 A F ice	125 C F loll	124 C F oth	123 C M pop	122 A M pop
89 A M pop	90 A M pop	91 A M pop	92 Y M oth	93 Y M loll	94 A F coke	95 OAP F ice	96 C F oth	97 OAP F oth	98 OAP F oth	99 C M loll
88 A M coke	87 A F choc	86 OAP M choc	85 OAP F choc	84 C M pop	83 C M pop	82 C F pop	81 C F pop	80 OAP F ice	79 OAP F ice	78 OAP M ice
45 A M oth	46 A F oth	47 OAP F ice	48 OAP M ice	49 Y M pop	50 A F pop	51 Y F pop	52 OAP F ice	53 OAP F ice	54 C F pop	55 Y F coke
44 A F coke	43 A F oth	42 C F oth	41 C F oth	40 C M oth	39 Y M coke	38 A M oth	37 C F loll	36 C F loll	35 OAP F choc	34 OAP M choc
1 C F choc	2 C F choc	3 OAP M choc	4 C F choc	5 C F choc	6 OAP F ice	7 OAP F ice	8 A F ice	9 A M ice	10 C F coke	11 C M pop

293 Y M coke	292 Y M coke	291 Y M coke	290 A M choc	289 A F choc	288 A M coke	287 A F coke				
276 Y M coke	277 Y M coke	278 Y M coke	279 Y M coke	280 A M oth	281 A F oth	282 A M pop	283 A F pop	284 A M ice	285 Y F pop	286 Y F pop
253 A F pop	252 A M choc	251 A F choc	250 A F choc	249 A M pop	248 A M pop	247 A M coke	246 A F coke	245 Y F pop	244 Y F pop	243 Y F pop
232 Y M pop	233 Y M pop	234 Y F pop	235 C F loll	236 C F loll	237 C F loll	238 Y M coke	239 Y F ice	240 A F ice	241 A M ice	242 A F ice
209 Y M pop	208 Y M pop	207 Y M pop	206 A M pop	205 C F pop	204 A F coke	203 A F oth	202 A M oth	201 A M oth	200 Y F coke	199 Y F coke
188 A M pop	189 A M pop	190 A M pop	191 C F oth	192 Y F pop	193 C F coke	194 OAP F oth	195 OAP M ice	196 C F pop	197 Y M coke	198 Y M coke
165 C F loll	164 C F loll	163 A M pop	162 OAP F choc	161 A F coke	160 C F pop	159 C M pop	158 OAP F choc	157 Y M choc	156 Y M choc	155 Y M choc
144 C M ice	145 OAP M ice	146 A M ice	147 OAP F ice	148 Y F ice	149 C F loll	150 C M choc	151 C M choc	152 A M choc	153 A M choc	154 A M choc
121 C M choc	120 C M choc	119 C F choc	118 C F loll	117 A F coke	116 A F coke	115 A F coke	114 OAP F coke	113 OAP M coke	112 C M coke	111 C M coke
100 OAP F ice	101 C F ice	102 Y F pop	103 A F coke	104 A M coke	105 A M coke	106 C F pop	107 C F pop	108 A F coke	109 A F coke	110 Y F coke
77 C F choc	76 C F choc	75 C F oth	74 OAP F oth	73 C F pop	72 C M loll	71 A F coke	70 A M coke	69 OAP M oth	68 C M choc	67 C M choc
56 C F loll	57 C F loll	58 Y F pop.	59 A F pop	60 A M pop	61 C M choc	62 OAP F choc	63 C F pop	64 C M pop	65 OAP M choc	66 A M pop
33 C M pop	32 C F pop	31 A F pop	30 A M ice	29 A M pop	28 C M loll	27 C M pop	26 A F pop	25 Y F coke	24 Y F pop	23 Y F pop
12 OAP F oth	13 C F pop	14 C M loll	15 C M loll	16 C F pop	17 C F choc	18 Y F pop	19 OAP M ice	20 A F ice	21 C M pop	22 C M choc

C Random number sampling

Another way to choose a sample of 30 is to use **random numbers**.

Random numbers are usually generated by a computer or a calculator.
Each figure from 0 to 9 has an equal chance of appearing.
On the opposite page are some random numbers which have been
arranged in groups of three digits to make them easy to use.

How to use the random numbers

Step 1: Decide where to start on the page.

Step 2: Decide whether to go up or down or left or right from that
position.

Step 3: Read the number at your starting point.

- If it is between 001 and 300, find the person in the audience on
pages 13 and 14 with that number. For example, 263 is

  263
  A
  F
  ice

- If the number is greater than 300, ignore it.

Type	Tally	Total
Popcorn		
Ice cream	/	
Lolly		
Choc bar		
Coke		
Other drink		

Record in a table that the person bought an ice cream.

Step 4: Choose the other 29 people in a similar way.

C1 Complete a table using the procedure described above in steps 1–4 and
advise the management what to stock. Remember to cater for 300 people.
Compare your results with those of other pupils.

C2 Steps 1 and 2 described above should really be carried out using a
random method. Otherwise you might always choose the same random
numbers. Suggest how you might carry out these steps at random.

Random numbers

134	466	245	207	263	368	007	782	626	293
652	676	429	510	473	352	221	859	427	273
095	998	600	133	657	990	038	968	335	301
728	245	440	953	118	124	057	354	020	869
042	128	727	325	570	413	326	250	672	281
870	180	598	936	154	574	108	593	568	235
316	246	538	440	762	931	699	721	476	211
298	157	943	591	693	386	672	745	487	771
399	874	227	719	818	511	122	739	327	311
561	480	107	652	872	549	021	775	808	685
295	662	741	267	083	976	385	274	339	417
933	257	383	936	485	951	233	561	193	157
956	951	544	319	312	929	907	849	340	544
657	132	436	467	931	546	435	759	636	213
902	733	439	784	955	487	172	648	340	234
902	942	456	134	778	138	954	483	861	633
997	406	292	055	721	941	695	161	479	264
878	756	911	697	189	269	420	076	788	858
462	417	749	737	792	548	184	863	152	424
667	981	434	092	492	808	984	677	911	586
364	294	588	330	767	638	760	061	544	575
076	625	089	927	126	888	168	077	341	157
931	005	721	826	422	283	743	291	618	169
495	063	992	671	966	192	229	234	264	643
207	558	893	904	072	945	702	976	794	182
024	062	090	071	298	153	673	889	239	262
598	721	382	978	709	300	019	534	320	960
480	899	664	338	601	058	010	420	071	606
542	686	754	415	489	623	433	948	689	232
353	558	452	358	757	272	055	120	181	452
738	490	490	121	591	303	497	424	886	954
346	478	009	259	589	828	073	415	822	739
685	687	476	306	645	665	556	556	713	760
724	705	428	807	409	617	431	924	850	303
444	496	758	957	309	983	019	205	570	700

D Could your sample be better?

The films shown at the cinema are currently placed in five different categories:

U
PG
12
15+
Over 18

Each category of film will be watched by an audience made up of different numbers of adults and children.

The quantities of each refreshment available at the kiosk may need to be varied according to the category of the film being shown.

Here is a pie chart showing the make-up (by age) of the audience for a U certificate film.

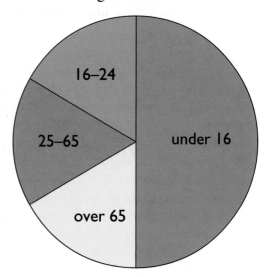

D1   Copy and complete the table below.

Ages of people	Angle of pie chart in degrees	Number in audience	Number in sample
under 16	180	$\frac{180}{360} \times 300 = 150$	15
16–24	60	$\frac{60}{360} \times 300 = 50$	5
25–65	60		
over 65			

To mimic the number in the whole cinema, the sample for U category films should contain:

15 people under 16

5 people 16–24

5 people 25–65

5 people over 65.

D2 Using random numbers, choose a sample made up as above. Pick a random number from the table (or elsewhere) and if it is less than 301 look up that seat in the cinema plan on pages 13 and 14. Once you have fifteen under 16 year olds, discard any others which get selected. Similarly, when you have five 16–24 year olds, discard extra people of that age group. Draw a frequency table (like the one on page 12) of the refreshments taken by the thirty people you select.

D3 Collate the information, interpret it and advise the management what to stock in the kiosk when U category films are showing.

D4 Use information from the following two pie charts to repeat questions **D2** and **D3** for these categories of films.

a *Over 18 films*   **b** *PG films*

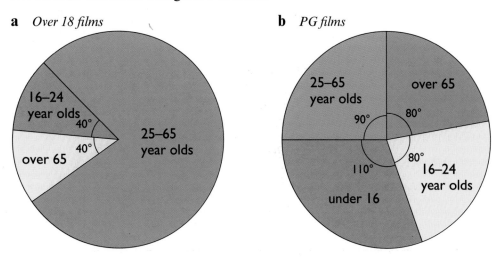

E Advertising campaign

E1   Enter the information about the 300 cinema-goers on pages 13 and 14 into a database.

You will need to:

- decide on field names
- decide on abbreviations and age codings
- design a data capture sheet
- divide up the task (small databases can often be merged into one big database).

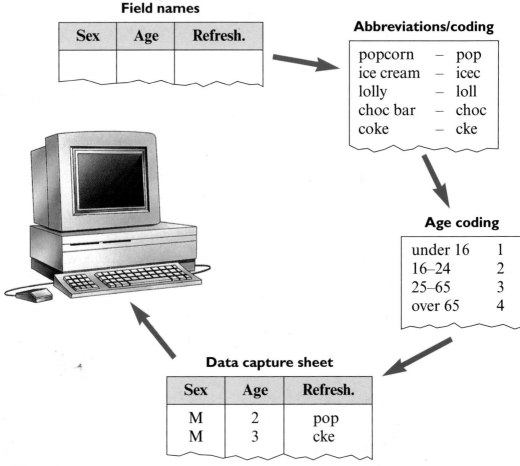

Field names

Sex	Age	Refresh.

Abbreviations/coding

popcorn	–	pop
ice cream	–	icec
lolly	–	loll
choc bar	–	choc
coke	–	cke

Age coding

under 16	1
16–24	2
25–65	3
over 65	4

Data capture sheet

Sex	Age	Refresh.
M	2	pop
M	3	cke

E2   Report on:

a   the percentage of each refreshment chosen

b   the percentage of each refreshment chosen by each age group

c   whether more men than women buy each product.

E3 **a** Choose one of the following projects:

Corn and Sons Ltd wish to run an advertising campaign to promote the sales of their popcorn. Advise them on a target audience and devise a suitable campaign.	Koolcoke Ltd wish to run an advertising campaign to promote sales of their cola. Advise them on a target audience and devise a suitable campaign.

Koolcream Ltd wish to run an advertising campaign to promote sales of their ice cream and lollies. Advise them on a target audience and devise a suitable campaign.	Choco Products wish to increase sales of their chocolate bars. Advise them on a target audience and devise a suitable campaign.

b Using the same methods as you used to find the answers to the cinema database searches, propose ways to solve the problem posed.

c Comment on the advantages and disadvantages of the company using the following.
   i posters
   ii magazine advertisements
   iii a radio jingle
   iv TV advertisements
   v another medium

UNIT 3 *Getting into groups*

A Discrete data

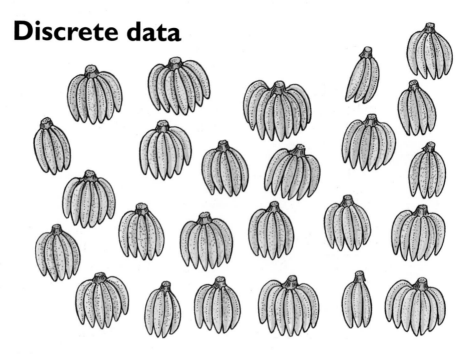

A banana ripener is interested in the number of bananas on each bunch. The picture above shows a box of bananas laid out. To get an overall picture, a tally or frequency chart can be used. To set this up, simply find the smallest (3) and largest (9) number of bananas on a bunch to know the limits.

The table looks like this:

Number of bananas	Total
3	2
4	4
5	7
6	8
7	3
8	0
9	1

When displaying data, the total or **frequency** is usually shown without tallies.

Remember that when the data consists of whole numbers, then the data is said to be **discrete**. When the data relates to a length or a temperature, it can be measured only as accurately as our instruments allow. Such data is called **continuous**.

A teacher is asked by the headteacher to look at absences in his class.
The number of times the 28 pupils in his class have been away in the last
year are:

13	8	12	17	24	8	0	15	11	18
2	7	14	31	16	10	5	19	21	14
12	0	2	15	16	7	14	15		

To put these figures in a frequency table like the opposite page would not
be very helpful. It makes more sense to put the data into groups. The
least number of days is 0 and the highest is 31. So a possible set of
groups would be:

0–9, 10–19, 20–29, 30–39

Putting the data in these groups gives:

Days	Frequency
0–9	9
10–19	16
20–29	2
30–39	1

Although it is clear that most people
have been away between 10 and 19
days, it is not very precise. It would,
perhaps, be better to use smaller
groups:

0–4, 5–9, 10–14, etc.

A1 Make and complete a table with these smaller groups.

Usually it is best to have at least five groups – but not too many.

A2 Put the following data into frequency tables. Choose appropriate groups.

a The number of day nursery places per 1000 under-fives in the
English counties:

11	7	3	1	4	9	7	0	5	8
1	4	4	6	3	3	26	22	4	2
7	1	0	1	17	9	3	21	1	3
2	4	9	3	0	3	5	2	2	13
0	15	0							

b The scores of batsmen playing first-class cricket in England on
a Saturday:

66	73	136	33	124	24	16	18	19	27
2	0	4	5	13	96	51	24	14	4
50	2	13	24	6	72	4	7	0	17
23	48	89	8	27	46	2	34	20	27
0	5	0	7	18	7	25	4	3	10

B Continuous data

A biologist is studying tadpoles. The picture below shows a sample that she has taken from a pond.

B1   Measure the lengths of the tadpoles in centimetres correct to 1 decimal place and write the measurements down. (The first one is 2.1 cm.)

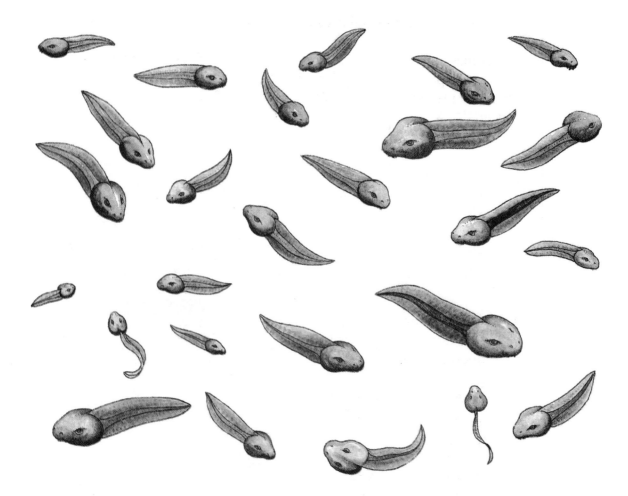

Groups are needed to put the measurements into a frequency table.

The smallest is 1.3 cm and the largest is 4.2 cm. If the groups are written 1–2, 2–3, etc.

what group would a length of 3.0 go into?

(Note: it is important that groups do not overlap, so take care with the group boundaries. Ensure that boundaries are decided to the same level of accuracy as the data and that group sizes are equal. See the opposite page.)

B2   One possible set of groups is shown in the left-hand column of this table:

Length (cm)	Frequency
1.0–1.9	
2.0–2.9	
3.0–3.9	
4.0–4.9	

Copy and complete the table using your measurements from question **B1**.

Sometimes, the final group needs to be **open-ended**. For example, if another tadpole of length 6.7 cm was included, rather than have a new group for just one tadpole, the final group might be altered to 4.0 or over.

However, it is a good idea to try to keep all the groups the same size.

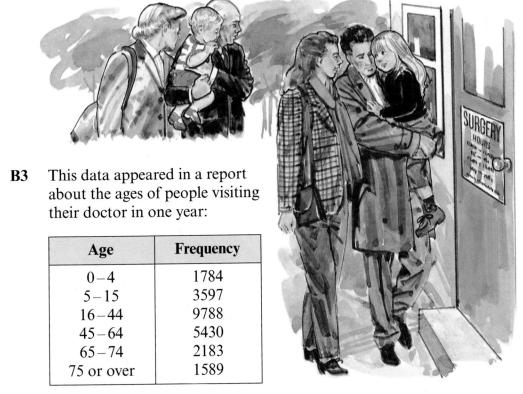

B3   This data appeared in a report about the ages of people visiting their doctor in one year:

Age	Frequency
0–4	1784
5–15	3597
16–44	9788
45–64	5430
65–74	2183
75 or over	1589

a   Can you tell from this data whether more toddlers or old people over 75 visited the doctor? (Some people may have made several visits.)

b   Is it more difficult to tell when groups are uneven?

c   Suggest reasons why the above groups were chosen.

C Changing groups

According to the World Bank, the populations of the main African states (excluding the Arab countries) are given in millions as:

1.1	33.1	1.1	44.8	32.6	14.6	8.3	10.9	7.8	5.0
6.8	15.7	5.7	3.2	6.4	3.8	4.3	2.7	22.1	23.1
1.6	106.6	13.6	1.9	2.3	7.0	9.0	11.1	2.0	10.9

Although the biggest is over 100 million, all the rest are less than 50 million. Here are two possible tables which could be used:

Table 1

Population (millions)	Frequency
0.0–4.9	10
5.0–9.9	8
10.0–14.9	5
15.0–19.9	1
20.0–24.9	2
25.0–29.9	0
30.0–34.9	2
35.0 and over	2

Table 2

Population (millions)	Frequency
0.0–9.9	18
10.0–19.9	6
20.0–29.9	2
30.0–39.9	2
40.0 and over	2

C1 Which of these tables most usefully describes the pattern of countries?

In this case, despite the problems of different sized groups, it might be sensible to use 0.0–4.9, 5.0–9.9 and then 10.0–19.9, etc. in larger groups.

C2 The distances from the Sun (in light years) of some of the most important asteroids are given in column q of the table below. Construct a frequency table of this data.

Name	Discoverer	Date	q	Name	Discoverer	Date	q
Ceres	Piazzi	1801	2.55	Cybele	Tempel	1861	3.01
Pallas	Olbers	1802	2.11	Undina	Peters	1867	2.97
Juno	Harding	1804	1.98	Arethusa	Luther	1867	2.61
Vesta	Olbers	1807	2.15	Bamberga	Palisa	1892	1.78
Astræa	Hencke	1845	2.10	Dembowska	Charlois	1892	2.66
Hebe	Hencke	1847	1.93	Eros	Witt	1898	1.13
Iris	Hind	1847	1.84	Patienta	Charlois	1899	2.82
Flora	Hind	1847	1.86	Davida	Dugan	1903	2.66
Metis	Graham	1848	2.09	Patroclus	Kopff	1906	4.48
Hygeia	De Gasparis	1849	2.84	Hector	Kopff	1907	4.99
Egeria	De Gasparis	1850	2.36	Interamnia	Cerulli	1910	2.58
Eunomia	De Gasparis	1851	2.15	Hidalgo	Baade	1920	2.00
Psyche	De Gasparis	1851	2.53	Æneas	Reinmuth	1930	4.64
Themis	De Gasparis	1853	2.76	Amor	Delporte	1932	1.08
Euphrosyne	Ferguson	1854	2.45	Icarus	Baade	1949	0.19
Nysa	Goldschmidt	1857	2.05	Apollo	Reinmuth	1932	0.65
Doris	Goldschmidt	1857	2.93	Chiron	Kowal	1977	8.50
Europa	Goldschmidt	1858	2.75	Moore	Bowell	1982	

Source: *The Guinness Book of Astronomy*

C3   The following table gives weather information around Great Britain.

Around Britain
Report for the 24 hours ended 6 pm yesterday

	Sun (hrs)	Rain (in)	Temp L H	Weather (day)		Sun (hrs)	Rain (in)	Temp L H	Weather (day)		Sun (hrs)	Rain (in)	Temp L H	Weather (day)
Aberdeen	-	0.17	3 7	Showers	Hayling Island	1.2	0.04	11 13	Rain	Ross-on-Wye	5.1	0.03	10 13	Sunny pm
Anglesey	6.8	0.50	7 11	Hail pm	Herne Bay	6.1	-	8 16	Sunny pm	Ryde	1.1	-	10 14	Showers
Aspatria	-	1.20	0 5	Rain	Hunstanton	1.6	-	6 17	Cloudy	Salcombe	7.2	0.07	10 13	Sunny pm
Aviemore	-	0.32	0 5	Showers	Isle Of Man	3.3	0.31	4 11	Rain am	Sandown	1.0	0.04	9 13	Rain pm
Belfast	-	0.65	2 5	Snow am	Isles of Scilly	9.0	0.02	7 11	Sunny	Saunton Sands	5.6	0.10	7 11	Sunny am
Birmingham	3.1	0.09	9 13	Rain am	Jersey	2.1	0.08	10 16	Rain pm	Scarborough	-	0.24	6 11	Rain
Bognor Regis	1.3	0.07	11 14	Shwrs pm	Kinloss	-	0.06	3 8	Showers	Shanklin	0.6	0.06	9 12	Rain pm
Bournemouth	2.5	0.03	10 14	Bright pm	Leeds	2.0	0.28	7 15	Rain	Skegness	2.0	-	8 15	Cloudy
Bristol	3.4	0.17	10 12	Sunny pm	Lerwick	10.6	0.05	2 8	Showers	Southend	3.0	-	9 16	Cloudy
Buxton	2.2	0.19	6 11	Showers	Leuchars	-	0.59	2 5	Rain	Southport	1.1	0.71	8 11	Rain
Cardiff	4.2	0.08	9 11	Shwrs pm	Littlehampton	1.4	0.07	10 13	Shwrs pm	Southsea	0.9	-	11 13	Rain pm
Clacton	2.7	-	8 15	Bright am	Liverpool	1.9	0.63	8 12	Shwr pm	Stornoway	9.8	0.07	2 8	Hail pm
Cleethorpes	1.8	0.06	8 15	Shwrs pm	London	1.6	0.06	11 15	Shwrs pm	Swanage	3.7	0.04	9 13	Showers
Cromer	1.9	-	7 17	Cloudy	Lowestoft	3.2	-	8 14	Sunny pm	Teignmouth	6.9	0.05	10 13	Sunny pm
Dunbar	-	1.09	3 5	Rain	Manchester	2.8	0.35	9 13	Rain am	Tenby	1.5	0.31	7 9	Cloudy
Eastbourne	3.1	0.03	10 15	Rain pm	Margate	6.2	-	8 17	Sunny pm	Tiree	6.4	0.01	3 9	Shwr pm
Edinburgh	-	1.52	2 5	Rain	Minehead	3.1	0.12	9 13	Bright pm	Torquay	6.3	0.04	10 14	Sunny pm
Eskdalemuir	-	1.07	0 2	Snow	Morecambe	0.7	1.25	5 11	Rain	Tynemouth	-	2.20	5 8	Rain
Exmouth	5.7	0.04	9 13	Sunny pm	Newcastle	-	2.46	5 8	Rain	Ventnor	0.3	0.10	10 12	Showers
Falmouth	7.2	0.23	9 12	Bright	Newquay	5.3	0.13	10 *		Weston-s-Mare	4.2	0.22	9 12	Sunny pm
Folkestone	3.6	-	9 14	Bright	Norwich	2.0	-	7 17	Cloudy	Weymouth	2.6	0.03	9 12	Bright pm
Glasgow	-	0.46	2 5	Rain	Nottingham	1.7	0.13	7 14	Rain am	Wick	3.7	0.07	1 9	Hail am
Guernsey	-	0.08	9 14	Showers	Penzance	9.4	0.11	9 11	Sunny	Worthing	2.8	0.07	10 13	Shwrs pm
Hastings	3.2	-	9 14	Bright pm	Plymouth	6.1	0.15	9 12	Bright	* reading not available.				
					Poole	2.7	0.05	9 12	Bright pm					

Source: *The Guardian* 15 May 1993

Construct frequency tables for the following:

a   the highest temperature, H (°C)

b   the hours of sunshine, Sun (hrs)

c   the rainfall in inches, Rain (in).

C4   The data below show the area in square miles of all current English counties.

Construct a frequency table using these figures.

Avon	520	Greater London	609	Northumberland	1942
Bedfordshire	477	Greater		North Yorkshire	3207
Berkshire	486	Manchester	497	Nottinghamshire	835
Buckinghamshire	727	Hampshire	1458	Oxfordshire	1007
Cambridgeshire	1316	Hereford and		Shropshire	1347
Cheshire	899	Worcester	1515	Somerset	1332
Cleveland	225	Hertfordshire	631	South Yorkshire	602
Cornwall	1376	Humberside	1356	Staffordshire	1048
Cumbria	2629	Isle of Wight	147	Suffolk	1466
Derbyshire	1016	Kent	1440	Surrey	648
Devon	2590	Lancashire	1182	Tyne and Wear	208
Dorset	1024	Leicestershire	985	Warwickshire	765
Durham	940	Lincolnshire	2283	West Midlands	347
East Sussex	693	Merseyside	252	West Sussex	768
Essex	1417	Norfolk	2072	West Yorkshire	787
Gloucestershire	1020	Northamptonshire	914	Wiltshire	1344

Source: *The State of the Nation*

D Stem and leaf

You met stem and leaf diagrams in the Handling Data 2 book.

The hours of sunshine in question **C3** can be recorded easily as:

```
 0 | 0 0 0 0 0 0 0 0 0 0 0 7 0 0 6 9 0 3
 1 | 3 8 9 2 6 4 9 6 7 1 0 1 5
 2 | 5 2 7 1 0 8 0 7 0 6 8
 3 | 1 4 1 6 2 3 2 1 0 7 7
 4 | 2 2
 5 | 7 3 1 6
 6 | 8 1 2 1 9 4 3
 7 | 2 2
 8 |
 9 | 0 4 8
10 | 6
```

Stem = 1.0, Leaf = 0.1

This can be organized even further by putting all the leaves in order.

```
 0 | 0 0 0 0 0 0 0 0 0 0 0 0 0 0 3 6 7 9
 1 | 0 1 1 2 3 4 5 6 6 7 8 9 9
 2 | 0 0 0 1 2 5 6 7 7 8 8
 3 | 0 1 1 1 2 2 3 4 6 7 7
 4 | 2 2
 5 | 1 3 6 7
 6 | 1 1 2 3 4 8 9
 7 | 2 2
 8 |
 9 | 0 4 8
10 | 6
```

Sometimes the numbers in each line of the stem and leaf may be split. For example, the following data of the life expectancy in some African countries is more clearly presented with smaller groups:

```
4 | 1
4 | 5 6 6 7 7 7 7 8 8 8 9
5 | 0 0 0 1 2 2 3 3 3
5 | 6 6 8 8 8 9 9
6 | 0
```

Stem = 10 years

With these adjustments, stem and leaf diagrams can usually be used instead of grouped frequency tables.

D1   Some people are interested in measuring their fitness. One measure of fitness is to do 'step ups' on to a 16 inch bench at a rate of 30 per minute for five minutes. After a rest of 1 minute, the pulse rate is taken for 30 seconds. The fitness index F is calculated by the formula:

F = (length of test in seconds) × 100/(pulse count for 30 secs × 5.5).

The results for a group of people were:

106	121	134	110	106	96	105	118	134	151
128	133	119	112	109	121	133	124	134	112
110	123	109	99	105	124	165	141	132	117

Construct a stem and leaf diagram for this data.

D2   Construct a stem and leaf diagram for the inches of rainfall from the weather data in question **C3**.

D3

Use the information below to construct a stem and leaf diagram of used car prices (£).

5995	7795	5995	6195	6295	5195	5850	6295	5850	4295
3550	3595	9995	9495	7495	6995	6995	4995	9495	7495
4795	6895	6450	5995	3495	8250	2995	9995	5995	4995
6895	5995	6995	2995	8995	5495	5195	2450	2450	6500

E Interpreting tables

Many official statistics are presented in large frequency tables. The following information looks at the daily newspapers read by people of different ages.

	Percentage of adults reading each paper in 1989			Percentage of each age group reading each paper in 1989				Readership (millions)	
	Males	Females	All adults	15–24	25–44	45–64	65 and over	1971	1989
Daily Newspapers									
The Sun	26	22	24	31	25	22	17	8.5	10.8
Daily Mirror	22	17	20	21	18	23	19	13.8	8.8
Daily Mail	10	9	10	8	9	11	10	4.8	4.3
Daily Express	9	8	9	7	7	11	10	9.7	3.9
Daily Star	7	4	6	8	7	5	3		2.7
The Daily Telegraph	6	5	6	3	4	8	7	3.6	2.5
The Guardian	4	2	3	3	4	3	1	1.1	1.3
Today	5	3	4	5	5	3	2		1.8
The Times	3	2	2	3	3	2	2	1.1	1.1
The Independent	3	2	3	3	3	2	1		1.2
Financial Times	2	1	2	1	2	2	–	0.7	0.7
Any daily newspaper	69	62	65	65	64	69	64		

Source: *Social Trends 21*, Central Statistical Office

The figures quoted are all percentages and are not affected by the fact that the age groups are of different sizes. Percentages adjust all groups so that you can think of all of them as of size 100.

There is a vast quantity of interesting information stored in this table.

For example:

A quarter of all people aged 25–44 read *The Sun*.
A higher percentage of men than women buy *The Sun*.
69% of all adults who buy a newspaper buy a tabloid (small size).
The readership of the *Daily Mirror* dropped by nearly a third from 1971 to 1989.

E1 Write down another fact about the newspapers which might be of interest.

E2 All 130 pupils in Year 10 at a school took an examination.
The maximum mark was 80.
The frequency distribution was as follows:

Marks	Frequency
1–10	8
11–20	15
21–30	23
31–40	10
41–50	25
51–60	26
61–70	16
71–80	7

Is this a typical year group? Explain your reasons.

E3 The ages of males and females in prisons in England and Wales in 1991 were given as:

Age in years	Males	Females
Under 21	5360	115
21–29	15008	464
30–39	8081	351
40–49	3743	162
50–59	1378	44
60 and over	396	12

Comment on the ages of males and females in prison.

UNIT 4 *Drawing an appropriate picture*

A Histograms and bar charts

Bar charts are often used to display discrete data or rounded continuous data. The bars need not touch and they can be either vertical or horizontal with the frequency shown on an axis in the same direction as the bars.

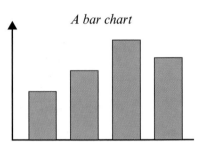

A bar chart

Histograms are often used to show the frequency of discrete data or continuous data but there are no gaps between the vertical bars.
The horizontal axis shows either discrete units or the class boundaries for continuous data. The vertical axis shows the frequency.

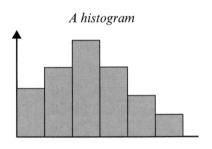

A histogram

A1 Decide if a bar chart or a histogram is more appropriate to show each of the following:

a the way people travel to school

b the heights of people in the class

c the class 'personal bests' for running 100 metres

d the amount of fish caught by a trawler

e the amount of petrol used by different vehicles

f the time for different kettles to boil a litre of water.

A2 Draw and label suitable axes for each part of question **A1**. For example, the axes for part **a** of the question might look like this:

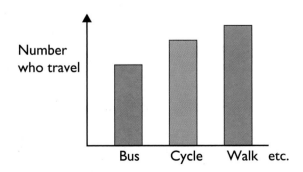

Number who travel

Bus   Cycle   Walk etc.

A3 Draw a bar chart or a histogram to illustrate the following data. In each case, state which type of chart you are using.

a Class 11Y were asked how they travelled to school. Here are their replies:

bus	cycle	bus	bus
walk	train	walk	car
walk	train	car	cycle
car	car	walk	walk
bus	cycle	cycle	walk
bus	bus	walk	walk

b In an experiment on reaction times, teenagers were asked to press a button when they saw a light start to flash. Here are their reaction times in seconds:

1.02	1.17	0.98	1.20	0.98	1.03
1.37	1.08	0.94	1.04	0.91	1.03
1.24	0.98	1.32	0.98	1.01	0.99

c Here are the dates of birth (day, month, year) of 21 Girl Guides:

14 04 84	04 07 84	20 11 83
27 08 84	18 05 84	23 02 84
16 10 83	19 12 83	12 08 84
07 05 84	07 12 83	13 12 83
27 06 84	16 09 83	12 10 83
25 12 83	16 05 84	18 04 84
27 02 84	17 04 84	11 12 83

d Here are the marks for Class 11Z in an examination:

24	26	20	18	24	27	30	19	23	19
24	26	30	28	25	25	26			

B Histograms and bar charts with a difference

Sometimes a normal bar chart or histogram is unable to show all the information properly.

For example:

'In the years 1990, 1991 and 1992 a show makes a profit of £50 000, £43 000 and £27 000, but in 1993 it makes a loss of £12 000.'

The *profit* can be shown on a diagram:

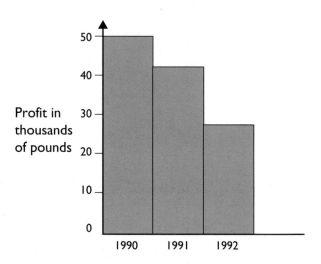

To show the *loss*, we need to extend the vertical scale downwards below 0, and include a block for the loss.

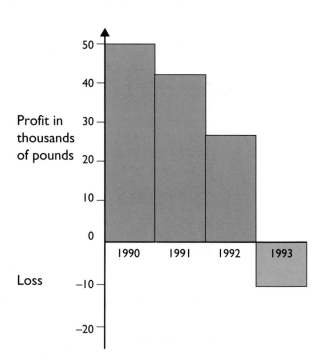

B1 Draw a chart for each of these sets of data:

a The profit made by Chocolike Ltd, a small chocolate factory, varies each month. Losses are shown in red.

January	February	March	April	May	June
£3000	£15 000	£22 000	£2000	£2000	£2000

July	August	September	October	November	December
£3000	£3000	£1000	£2000	£36 000	£40 000

Can you explain the pattern shown?

b The average (mean) temperature at the centre of the island in degrees Celsius is recorded below:

January to March	April to June	July to September	October to December
–2°	15°	20°	8°

c

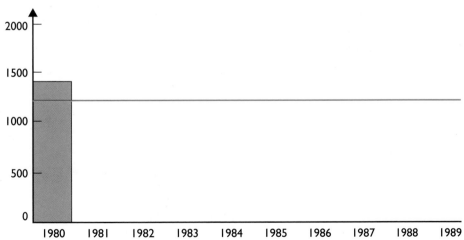

The average annual production of beef (in thousands of tonnes) from European Community countries is given below:

1980	1981	1982	1983	1984	1985	1986	1987	1988	1989
1400	1000	1050	950	1800	1500	1100	1100	700	1400

(Note: the line across at 1200 represents the overall average annual beef production.)

C Compound bar charts

These bar charts give information about the use made of the land on two farms.

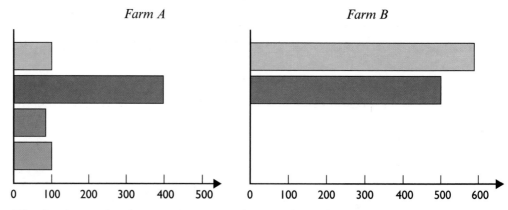

The horizontal columns represent the number of hectares used for:

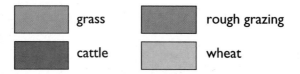

The same information could have been shown as a **compound bar chart**.

To draw a compound bar chart:

Step 1: Set up a scale large enough to allow for all the individual bars to be placed end to end.

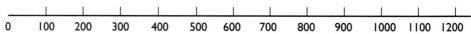

Step 2: Draw the first bar for Farm A.

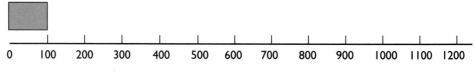

Step 3: Add the second bar.

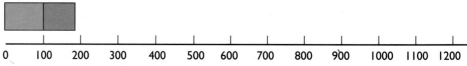

Step 4: Add the other bars.

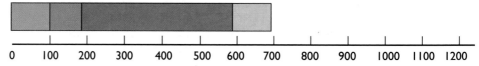

Step 5: Draw a compound bar chart for Farm B.

Step 6: Put the two bar charts together:

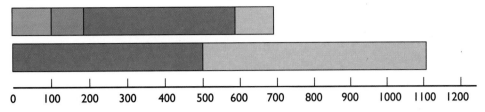

It is now easy to see that Farm A is almost half the size of Farm B and that proportionately more land is given up to cattle.

C1 Draw compound bar charts to represent the following information:

a A chocolate factory sells its sweets in Britain, the EU and the USA. Prepare a compound bar chart, like the one above, for the years 1990 and 1991.

Sales in thousands of £	Britain	EU	USA
1990	4	1.5	1
1991	4	2.5	1.5

b The local council is concerned about road safety and is trying to reduce speeding in its area. They have obtained the following information about stopping distances for use in a publicity campaign and would like to represent it in a compound bar chart.

Stopping distances in metres				
Speed in k.p.h.	50	60	70	80
dry road	26	35	45	63
wet road	55	72	100	130

D Getting more information from bar charts

D1 Here is a vertical compound bar chart showing the changes of use of a piece of agricultural land over a ten-year period.

Describe the information shown.

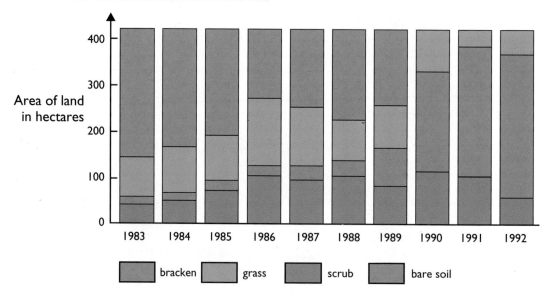

D2 Produce a vertical compound bar chart for the cinema data that you found in question **D2** on page 18.

Choose a suitable scale on the vertical axis for the number consumed. (Note: the graph below is just for illustration. The figures are not the same as you will use.)

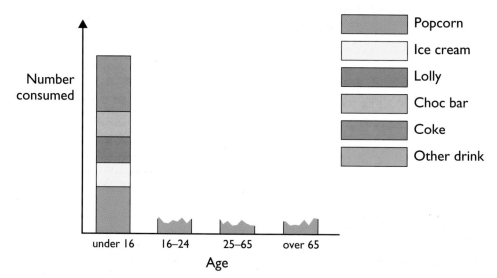

Pyramids

Sometimes, bar charts are drawn back-to-back to allow comparisons to be made between two sets of data. You met an example on page 9.

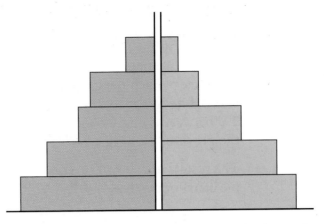

A common use for these 'pyramids' is to show the ages of two populations.

The vertical axis represents the age groups. The horizontal axis shows the number in each age group in each population.

D3 Prepare axes like those below, with suitable scales to illustrate the data in the table below.

Age range in years	0–9	10–19	20–29	30–39	40–49	50–59	60–69	70–79	over 79
Male population in millions	20.2	15.5	11.3	12.6	11.9	10.1	7.5	4.8	0.9
Female population in millions	18.8	14.2	10.3	12.0	10.3	9.3	7.2	5.4	1.0

E   Don't forget the pie charts

E1   A survey of the TV watching habits of 600 people was conducted. Each person was asked if he or she had watched TV between 5 and 6 o'clock the previous evening.

The results are shown on the pie chart opposite.

Measure the angles and use the headings below to calculate how many people watched each channel.

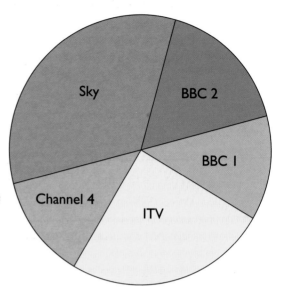

Channel	Angle	Fraction	Number of people
ITV	90°	$\frac{90}{360} = \frac{1}{4}$	$\frac{1}{4}$ of 600 = 150
Channel 4	45°	$\frac{45}{360}$	

E2   A village has a population of 1800 people of working age. The pie chart represents the types of job they have.

Measure the angles and then calculate how many are in each category.

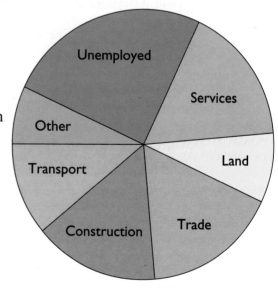

Type of occupation	Angle	Fraction	Number of people
Unemployed	90°	$\frac{90}{360} = \frac{1}{4}$	$\frac{1}{4}$ of 1800 = 450
Services			

Use the information in the tables on this page to construct pie charts.

Make a copy of each table. Calculate each angle and then draw the pie chart.

E3   The holiday destinations of 180 families were as shown in the table:

Holiday destination	Number of families	Fraction	Angle
Britain	48		
USA	16		
Europe	64		
Others	52		
Total			

E4   A typical pupil's day is spent on the following activities:

Activity	Time in hours	Fraction	Angle
Sleeping	10		
School	7		
Watching TV	3		
Doing homework	1		
Others	3		
Total			

E5   The land mass of the largest continents are shown below:

Continent	Area in millions km²	Fraction	Angle
Asia	44.5		
Europe	10.5		
Africa	30.5		
America	42.0		
Others	22.5		
Total			

UNIT 5 *Is there a connection?*

A Finding trends

When you have collected information, finding trends and relationships in the data is the next stage. It is often useful to draw a chart in order to do this.

For example, to find out if the biggest pebbles are to be found furthest up the beach from the sea, a sample of pebbles was taken every 2 metres up a beach, starting at the low tide mark. The average weight of the pebbles in each sample was found. The results are given below:

Distance from sea in metres	0	2	4	6	8	10
Average weight in grams	12.6	11.8	16.8	20.8	18.2	22.4

A scatter graph is drawn by choosing suitable axes and plotting each of the results as a cross on the graph, as follows:

First, draw suitable axes.

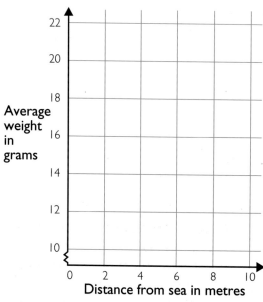

(Remember to label axes and to say what scale you are using.)

Then plot the six
results with crosses:

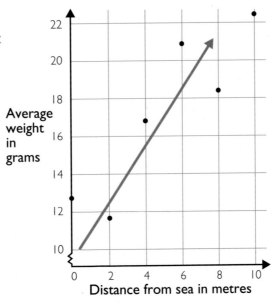

The scatter graph shows that there is a general trend for the larger
pebbles to be further up the beach away from the sea. This trend is
indicated by the red arrow.

Do not expect the plotted points to be in a straight line.

Scatter graphs (sometimes called scatter diagrams) may indicate a
relationship between the two measures they portray. Such a relationship
may be very marked or only slight. They may also show that there is no
relationship at all.

Look at these three scatter graphs:

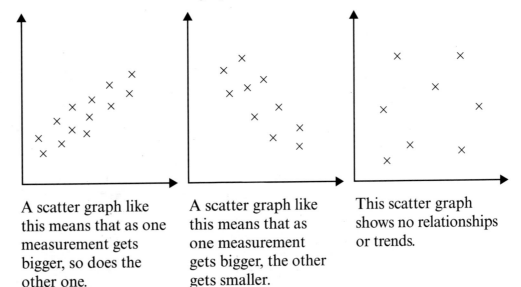

A scatter graph like
this means that as one
measurement gets
bigger, so does the
other one.

A scatter graph like
this means that as
one measurement
gets bigger, the other
gets smaller.

This scatter graph
shows no relationships
or trends.

The first two graphs show a **correlation** between the two measures or
variables which are being compared.

A1 Write a sentence to say what each of these scatter graphs suggests about
the two measures.

a *Data on heights of mothers and children*

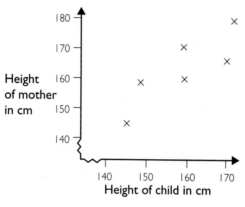

b *Information showing travel times of trains*

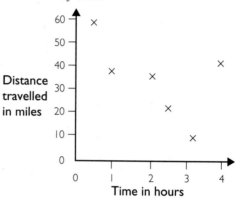

c *Information showing travelling times of commuters arriving at destinations*

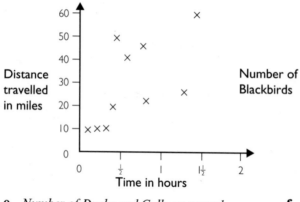

d *Survey of Blackbirds and Magpies in a park*

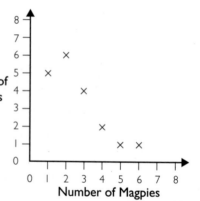

e *Number of Ducks and Gulls on a pond in Xshire*

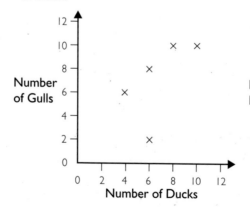

f *Marks in French and marks in Mathematics*

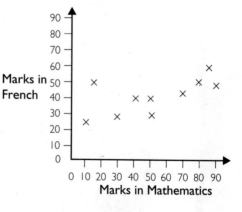

A2 Explain the relationships (if any) which the graphs above suggest?
Discuss and compare your explanations with other pupils.

A3 Draw a scatter graph for each of the sets of data below and then comment on the hypothesis stated. (A hypothesis is a statement that is made as a starting point for further investigation from the known facts.)

a *Hypothesis*: The more hours of sunshine, the higher the average temperature.

Hours of sunshine	11	11	13	10	15	8	7	6
Average temperature in°C	15	16	14	10	14	9	13	11

b *Hypothesis*: The longer leaves are at the top of the tree.

Distance from ground in cm	200	210	220	230	240	250
Length of leaf in cm	11.8	12.5	13.3	12.9	12.8	13.5

c *Hypothesis*: The biggest strawberries are near the edge of the field.

Distance from edge of field in metres	5.3	6.2	11.3	14.4	5.8	12.7	11.9
Size of strawberry in grams	12.0	12.3	13.3	10.3	7.2	11.8	10.4

d *Hypothesis*: The biggest horses run fastest.

Height of horse in hands *	17.2	16.2	15.8	16.4	16.8	17.0	15.3	15.0
Place in race	1	2	3	4	5	6	7	8

* A 'hand' is a unit in which the height of a horse may be measured. One hand is 4 inches, approximately 10 cm.

B How to find trends

Lesley has just started a
Saturday job in Better
Clothes. She notices that
jeans for women are
sized as 10, 12, 14 and 16
while jeans for men are
sized 30, 32, 34, etc.

For her textiles project, she has decided to investigate the sizing of jeans.
She has collected body measurements from pupils in her school and
produced scatter graphs to see if there are any relationships between the
different measurements.

Her list of body measurements is given on the next page.

B1 Use a computer graphics program to help you produce scatter graphs
illustrating Lesley's findings.
What conclusions can you draw from the graphs?

Body measurements of pupils in Lesley's school

Number	Sex	Waist in cm	Hip in cm	Outside leg in cm	Number	Sex	Waist in cm	Hip in cm	Outside leg in cm
1	M	67	72	80	25	M	80	95	95
2	M	69	76	83	26	M	85	96	98
3	M	64	86	81	27	F	56	86	105
4	M	78	86	86	28	M	83	96	91
5	F	61	92	105	29	M	74	94	94
6	F	66	86	111	30	F	56	86	99
7	M	73	87	90	31	F	59	83	96
8	M	78	89	90	32	M	77	94	90
9	F	70	102	108	33	F	56	82	98
10	M	70	91	85	34	F	59	85	106
11	F	75	111	105	35	M	87	97	101
12	F	65	96	96	36	F	53	75	98
13	F	66	94	100	37	M	95	97	102
14	M	75	91	95	38	M	84	100	95
15	M	86	91	93	39	F	54	75	106
16	M	84	92	110	40	F	57	80	111
17	M	79	92	98	41	F	75	96	103
18	M	76	93	96	42	M	90	101	97
19	F	70	95	103	43	M	88	103	103
20	F	71	96	101	44	M	90	110	95
21	F	72	100	102	45	M	90	114	100
22	F	71	106	100	46	F	60	92	61
23	F	69	94	107					
24	M	82	94	94					

C A shirty problem

C1 Investigate *either*

  a the sizing of shirts *or*

  b why men's shirts are sized by collar size and women's shirts by bust measurement.

Use the measurements below, or collect your own, to see if there is a relationship between the different body measurements.

Try to explain the sizing of shirts.

Sex	Neck Measurement in cm	Chest Measurement in cm	Arm Measurement in cm	Back Measurement in cm
F	36.5	86.5	52	39.5
M	38.5	81.5	57.5	50.5
M	32.5	84.5	46.5	44.5
M	38.5	90.5	52.5	49.5
M	38	90.5	55.5	46.5
M	39	80.5	53.5	46
M	37	79.5	58.5	45
M	35.5	83.5	57	49.5
M	37	85.5	54.5	43.5
M	45	80.5	49.5	42.5
F	33.5	80.5	52.5	42
F	36	80.5	55	40.5
F	35	85.5	53.5	44.5
M	42.5	96.5	55.5	47.5
M	35.5	74.5	51	39.5
M	31.5	72.5	50.5	40.5
F	31	82.5	53.5	41
F	31.5	84.5	54.5	38.5
F	37.5	83.5	51.5	36.5
M	37.5	87.5	56.5	43.5
M	33	77.5	54.5	37.5
M	34.5	82	60	47
M	33.5	95.5	58	44.5
M	37.5	81.5	57.5	44
F	33.5	83.5	55.5	44
M	37	89.5	53.5	46.5
M	38.5	81.5	61.5	49.5
M	38	93	55.5	41.5
M	40.5	89.5	55.5	46.5
F	36	82.5	54.5	46.5
M	35.5	82.5	57.5	44.5
M	32	73.5	55	40.5
M	35	93.5	56.5	43.5
M	34.5	87	53.5	45
M	37.5	92.5	56.5	45
F	36.5	84.5	51.5	40.5
F	36.5	85.5	51.5	41
F	34.5	86.5	52	41.5
F	33.5	87	52.5	41.5
F	32.5	87.5	53	42

Sex	Neck measurement in cm	Chest measurement in cm	Arm measurement in cm	Back measurement in cm
F	31.5	88.5	53.5	42.5
F	36.5	85.5	51.5	40.5
F	31.5	89.5	53.5	42.5
F	33.5	87.5	52.5	41.5
F	32.5	86.5	53	42
F	31.5	88.5	53.5	42.5
F	31.5	87.5	53.5	42.5
F	35.5	84.5	51.5	41
F	32.5	85	51.5	41
F	34.5	85.5	52	42
F	34.5	78.5	54.5	38.5
F	34.5	79.5	44.5	35.5
F	34.5	87	53.5	45
F	32	87.5	55.5	40.5
F	32.5	87.5	51	39.5
M	37.5	82.5	54.5	48.5
M	33.5	77.5	54.5	43.5
M	40	82.5	55.5	45
M	34	76.5	55.5	46
M	36.5	83	57.5	45
F	35.5	94.5	49.5	42.5
F	36.5	94	52	40.5
F	36.5	93.5	47.5	42.5
M	33.5	73.5	53	44
M	36.5	79	56	47.5
M	34.5	79	58.5	42.5
M	37.5	100.5	59.5	42.5
M	34.5	83.5	55	40.5
M	34	74	55.5	46
M	33.5	87.5	56.5	43
M	37.5	76.5	57.5	43.5
M	34.5	75.5	53	41.5
F	32.5	90.5	54.5	40.5
F	31.5	88.5	50.5	45
F	35.5	88	56.5	46.5
F	32	88.5	50.5	42.5
F	33.5	87.5	56.5	47.5
M	38.5	86	62	47
M	35.5	79.5	55.5	43.5
M	36.5	83.5	55.5	41.5
M	37.5	81.5	53	45.5
M	31.5	75.5	48.5	38.5
F	33.5	79.5	50.5	44.5
F	34.5	79.5	53.5	40.5
F	31	82.5	49.5	37.5
M	35.5	98.5	51	40
M	34.5	97.5	55.5	42
M	36.5	95	53	46.5
M	31.5	81.5	44.5	46
M	34.5	89.5	52.5	36.5
M	31.5	85.5	55.5	39.5
M	32.5	81.5	55.5	36.5
M	35.5	98.5	54.5	39.5
F	33	80.5	47.5	43
F	32.5	80.5	52	40.5
M	32.5	92.5	50.5	32.5
M	34.5	99.5	50.5	35.5
F	37	84.5	56.5	46.5
M	39.5	87.5	69.5	49.5

D Does age matter?

D1   **Extension work** The older pupils in each school year can be nearly twelve months older than the younger pupils. Does this matter by the age of 16? (In the table, each pupil's total score is obtained by converting examination grades to numbers where
A = 7, B = 6, C = 5, D = 4, E = 3, F = 2, G = 1.)

Using the results below, try to answer this question: are the older children getting better results?

A computer package, possibly a spreadsheet, may help you.

spreadsheet

Pupil's birth	Number of subjects	Total score	Average score	Pupil's birth	Number of subjects	Total score	Average score
09/05/76	9	48	5.33	02/10/75	9	60	6.67
12/10/75	8	51	6.38	15/02/76	8	45	5.63
14/08/76	8	51	6.38	28/02/76	8	48	6.00
14/04/76	8	34	4.25	27/08/76	8	50	6.25
27/11/75	8	52	6.50	23/05/76	8	47	5.88
07/12/75	9	56	6.22	16/02/76	9	63	7.00
31/07/76	8	50	6.25	24/03/76	9	61	6.78
15/05/76	8	47	5.88	02/05/76	9	57	6.33
20/01/76	8	53	6.63	18/04/76	8	48	6.00
30/06/76	8	53	6.63	11/04/76	9	56	6.22
03/02/76	8	55	6.88	16/12/75	8	50	6.25
01/09/75	9	62	6.89	30/11/75	8	47	5.88
20/11/75	9	55	6.11	28/04/76	8	52	6.50
16/03/76	9	57	6.33	09/12/75	9	63	7.00
12/10/75	8	48	6.00	19/04/76	9	60	6.67
27/01/76	8	47	5.88	07/06/76	8	47	5.88
02/09/75	8	39	4.88	30/12/75	9	59	6.56
14/09/75	8	48	6.00	08/09/75	9	62	6.89
18/04/76	9	58	6.44	19/04/76	9	63	7.00
17/10/75	9	62	6.89	18/06/76	8	50	6.25
07/11/75	9	57	6.33	25/03/76	9	48	5.33
20/07/76	9	59	6.56	15/01/76	9	62	6.89
02/10/75	8	54	6.75	02/01/76	8	48	6.00
29/01/76	9	60	6.67	19/03/76	9	63	7.00
17/12/75	9	59	6.56	21/01/76	8	53	6.63
12/06/76	9	44	4.89	26/08/75	8	49	6.13
04/02/76	8	41	5.13	19/03/76	8	40	5.00
23/05/76	8	34	4.25	16/04/75	7	46	6.57
22/07/76	8	37	4.63	18/02/76	9	45	5.00
22/11/75	9	62	6.89	17/06/76	8	51	6.38
07/03/76	9	62	6.89	06/01/76	8	43	5.38
03/04/76	8	43	5.38	31/05/76	8	47	5.88
18/01/76	8	35	4.38	18/12/75	9	59	6.56
17/12/75	8	46	5.75	29/06/76	8	47	5.88
30/08/76	9	62	6.89	16/12/75	8	52	6.50
23/03/76	8	45	5.63	18/04/76	8	49	6.13
28/12/75	7	35	5.00	29/06/76	8	40	5.00
16/02/76	9	63	7.00	03/01/76	9	55	6.11
05/02/76	8	53	6.63	07/03/76	8	35	4.38
12/11/75	8	48	6.00	29/03/76	8	36	4.50
12/06/76	9	59	6.56	11/03/76	9	56	6.22
08/10/75	8	44	5.50	12/08/76	8	36	4.50
29/06/75	8	50	6.25	21/09/75	9	62	6.89

Pupil's birth	Number of subjects	Total score	Average score	Pupil's birth	Number of subjects	Total score	Average score
20/04/76	8	49	6.13	08/12/75	8	49	6.13
01/05/76	8	38	4.75	01/04/76	9	58	6.44
18/10/75	9	63	7.00	06/10/75	9	57	6.33
04/03/76	9	61	6.78	15/06/76	9	63	7.00
02/07/76	9	41	4.56	10/10/75	9	48	5.33
11/02/76	9	59	6.56	01/07/76	9	63	7.00
24/04/76	8	50	6.25	10/12/75	9	56	6.22
11/07/76	8	51	6.38	02/08/76	8	42	5.25
01/08/76	9	53	5.89	13/02/75	9	60	6.67
26/01/76	8	45	5.63	29/04/76	8	50	6.25
11/07/76	9	55	6.11	03/07/76	9	57	6.33
25/10/75	8	53	6.63	13/09/75	9	58	6.44
14/07/76	8	39	4.88	18/06/76	8	50	6.25
05/01/76	8	46	5.75	25/03/76	9	48	5.33
19/07/76	8	49	6.13	15/01/76	9	62	6.89
03/11/75	9	56	6.22	02/01/76	8	48	6.00
11/12/75	8	45	5.63	19/03/76	9	63	7.00
10/06/76	8	46	5.75	21/01/76	8	53	6.63
13/04/76	9	63	7.00	26/08/76	8	49	6.13
11/04/76	8	54	6.75	19/03/76	8	40	5.00
10/05/76	8	48	6.00	19/02/76	9	45	5.00
14/05/76	9	60	6.67	19/02/76	9	45	5.00
10/01/76	9	57	6.33	28/06/76	8	51	6.38
28/09/75	8	48	6.00	07/01/76	8	43	5.38
13/02/76	9	63	7.00	31/05/76	8	47	5.88
24/03/76	9	61	6.78	18/12/74	9	59	6.56
11/03/75	9	58	6.44	29/06/76	8	47	5.88
27/03/76	8	52	6.50	16/12/75	8	52	6.50
07/04/76	8	44	5.50	18/04/76	8	49	6.13
03/06/76	8	49	6.13	29/06/76	8	40	5.00
24/12/75	8	48	6.00	03/01/76	9	55	6.11
25/03/76	8	45	5.63	07/03/76	8	35	4.38
19/03/76	9	63	7.00	29/03/76	8	36	4.50
12/09/75	9	50	5.56	11/03/76	9	56	6.22
30/07/76	8	50	6.25	12/08/76	8	36	4.50
18/05/76	8	44	5.50	21/09/75	9	62	6.89
16/09/75	9	63	7.00	08/12/75	8	49	6.13
04/06/76	8	49	6.13	01/04/76	9	58	6.44
13/02/76	8	48	6.00	06/10/75	9	57	6.33
11/04/76	8	48	6.00	15/06/76	9	63	7.00
14/01/76	8	39	4.88	10/10/75	9	48	5.33
04/08/76	8	47	5.88	01/07/76	9	63	7.00
16/08/76	8	46	5.75	10/12/75	9	56	6.22
10/08/76	9	60	6.67	02/08/76	8	42	5.25
03/07/76	8	44	5.50	13/02/76	9	60	6.67
12/03/75	8	49	6.13	29/04/76	8	50	6.25
04/10/75	9	62	6.89	03/07/76	9	57	6.33
02/12/75	9	63	7.00	13/09/75	9	58	6.44
19/02/75	8	44	5.50	16/04/75	7	46	6.57
02/03/76	8	45	5.63	19/04/76	9	63	7.00
23/01/76	8	53	6.63	26/02/76	9	62	6.89
19/06/76	8	50	6.25	27/09/75	8	39	4.88
02/10/75	9	60	6.67	15/02/76	8	45	5.63
28/02/76	8	48	6.00	27/08/76	8	50	6.25
23/05/76	8	47	5.88	16/02/76	9	63	7.00
24/03/76	9	61	6.78	02/05/76	9	57	6.33
18/04/76	8	48	6.00	11/04/76	9	56	6.22
16/12/75	8	50	6.25	30/11/75	8	47	5.88
28/04/76	8	52	6.50	09/12/75	9	63	7.00
19/04/76	9	60	6.67	07/06/76	8	47	5.88
30/12/75	9	59	6.56	08/09/75	9	62	6.89

UNIT 6   *Tables, scales and networks*

A Two-way tables

The results of a test are displayed in this table.

Boys who failed test

Girls who passed test

Total

	Boys	Girls	Totals
Passed	12	13	25
Failed	8	17	25
Totals	20	30	50

The following paragraph describes the results in the table:

> Almost equal numbers of boys and girls passed the test, but twice as many girls failed as boys. Thirty girls took part, but only twenty boys.

The information in the paragraph can be misleading, even though it is true. The table allows the information to be studied closely and features identified exactly.

A1 Write a paragraph to describe the information in these tables:

a

	Sheep	Cows	Totals
Sold	200	100	300
Unsold	20	20	40
Totals	220	120	340

b

	Athletes	Swimmers	Totals
Scotland	32	18	50
England	48	2	50
Totals	80	20	100

c

	Do like ice cream	Don't like ice cream	Totals
Boys	25	5	30
Girls	15	15	30
Totals	40	20	60

d

	Won	Lost	Drawn	Totals
A team	8	8	4	20
B team	12	6	2	20
Totals	20	14	6	40

A2 Make a copy of the table below.

Use the information on pages 13 and 14 of the cinema kiosk investigation in Unit 2 to fill in the table.

Ages of people	Popcorn	Ice cream	Lolly	Choc bar	Coke	Other drink	Totals
under 16							
16-24							
25-65							
over 65							

A3 Write a description of the information in your completed table.

Because there is a different number in each age group, it may be easier to make comparisons if percentages of each age group are used. For example, to find the percentage of under 16s who have popcorn, divide the number of under 16s who have popcorn by the total number of under 16s and multiply by 100.

A4 Rewrite the table prepared in question **A2** using percentages.

A5 Rewrite the description prepared in question **A3** using the information in the new table.

B Timetables

Timetables give information about the arrival and departure times of buses, trains and aeroplanes. For buses, there is usually only one time given on the timetable as they tend to arrive at a stop, set people down, pick people up and depart as soon as they can, so a departure time is not necessary.

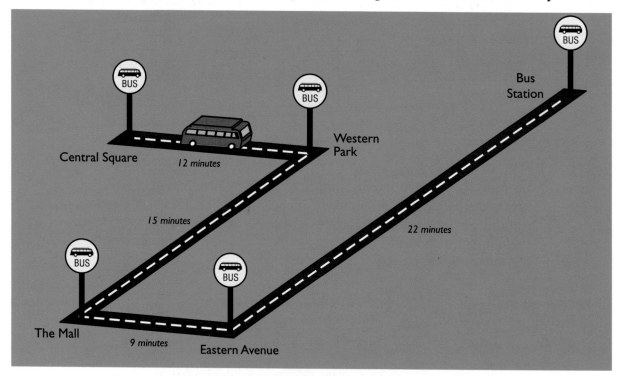

	Bus 1	Bus 2	Bus 3	Bus 4	Bus 5
Central Square	06.05	06.25	06.45	07.05	07.25
Western Park	06.17	06.37	06.57	07.17	07.37
The Mall	06.32	06.52	07.12	07.32	07.52
Eastern Avenue	06.41	07.01	07.21	07.41	08.01
Bus Station	07.03	07.23	07.43	08.03	08.23
Bus Station	06.30	06.50			
Eastern Avenue	06.52				
The Mall	07.01				
Western Park					
Central Square					

B1 Copy and complete the return journey timetable from the Bus Station to Central Square. Assume that buses return at the same frequency and take the same time on the return journey.

B2 Which bus must I catch from Central Square if I wish to be at The Mall for half past seven?

B3 If I catch the five minutes past seven bus, when will I arrive at Eastern Avenue?

B4 How long does it take to get from Central Square to Eastern Avenue?

B5 Where on the route does the five minutes past six bus from Central Square pass the half past six bus from the Bus Station?

B6 When does the half past seven bus from the Bus Station get to Western Park?

B7 How long does it take to get from The Mall to Central Square?

In the South Island of New Zealand, there is a train that runs between Christchurch and Dunedin. Here is a page of the timetable:

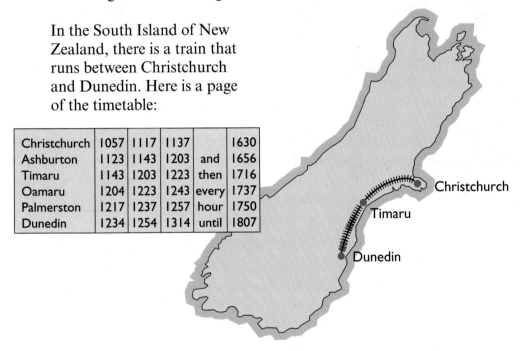

Christchurch	1057	1117	1137		1630
Ashburton	1123	1143	1203	and	1656
Timaru	1143	1203	1223	then	1716
Oamaru	1204	1223	1243	every	1737
Palmerston	1217	1237	1257	hour	1750
Dunedin	1234	1254	1314	until	1807

B8 If I have to be in Dunedin by half past two, which train must I catch from Christchurch?

B9 I am at Timaru. The time is mid-day. When will the next train arrive and how long will it be before I am in Dunedin?

B10 I have to be in Palmerston at six o'clock in the afternoon. Which train do I catch from Oamaru?

B11 Which two neighbouring towns on the route are furthest apart? (Assume the train travels at the same speed throughout.)

C More information tables

The distances in kilometres between a number of towns can be shown in a triangle-shaped table like the following:

Amberton					
77	Beacon				
14	70	Coldfield			
54	34	24	Littlecroft		
84	83	67	66	Barnhead	
100	93	81	53	17	Tolmouth

This is the distance between Beacon and Littlecroft

This is the distance between Amberton Tolworth

This is the distance between Coldfield and Tolmouth

C1 How far is it between Amberton and Littlecroft?

C2 What is the distance between Beacon and Tolmouth?

C3 Is the distance between Coldfield and Barnhead greater or smaller than that between Barnhead and Beacon?

C4 Make copies of the tables below.
Use the sketch map to complete the tables.
Use the shortest distances.

a

Ackfield				
	Mountby			
		Great Yarby		
	31		Tunton	
		44		Mucklefield

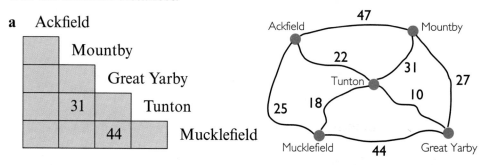

b

Chuter				
	Hunton			
		Broadhurst		
			Crowhead	
				Waterford

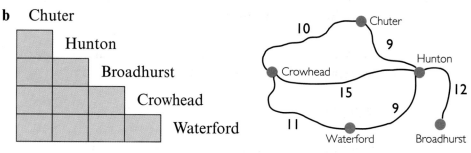

Here is a credit repayment table which is used to calculate the monthly repayments to be paid over three different periods of time.

Money to be repaid (£)	Monthly Repayments over		
	12 months	24 months	36 months
50	6.10	4.00	3.30
100	11.10	6.90	5.50
200	21.20	12.80	10.00
300	31.20	18.70	14.50
400	41.30	24.60	19.00
500	51.40	30.50	23.50
600	61.50	36.50	28.00
700	71.50	42.40	32.70
800	81.60	48.30	37.20
900	91.70	54.20	41.70
1000	101.80	60.10	46.20
2000	202.60	119.20	91.40
3000	303.40	178.30	136.60
4000	404.20	237.40	181.80
5000	505.00	296.50	227.00
6000	605.80	355.60	272.20
7000	706.60	414.70	317.40
8000	807.40	473.80	362.60
9000	908.20	532.90	407.80

Easy Hire-purchase Terms Arranged on All Goods!

LOANS ARRANGED

Repayments over 12 Months

FLEXIBLE 2-year Loans

36 Months to Repay

C5 Mr Briggs has bought a new car and has £8400 to repay. What will the monthly repayments be if he pays over

    a 12 months   **b** 24 months   **c** 36 months?

C6 Wayne borrowed £150 to buy a leather coat. What will his repayments be if he pays back over 12 months?

C7 Mrs Brown bought a new three-piece suite with a loan of £1200. What are her repayments over 36 months?

C8 If Sue pays back £119.20 for 24 months, how much did she borrow?

C9 For 36 months, Rajiv pays £309.40 each month. How much did he borrow?

D Scales

Converting one scale into another can be done easily on a scale diagram.

Here is a chart for pounds weight and kilograms:

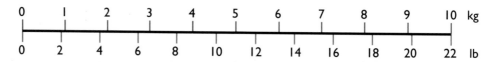

This chart links temperature in °Celsius and °Fahrenheit:

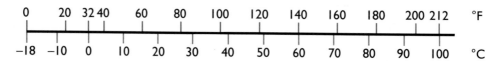

This scale is useful for converting fractions into decimals or vice versa:

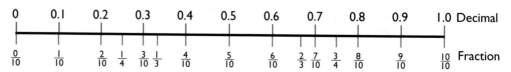

D1   Copy the values below and use the scales above to decide whether to put
< (is less than) or > (is greater than) in each gap.

a 4 lb   2 kg

b 6 lb   12 kg

c 125°F   50°C

d 150°F   60°C

e $\frac{2}{5}$ 0.3

f 0.7 $\frac{2}{3}$

g $\frac{3}{10}$ $\frac{1}{3}$

h 200°F   90°C

i 18 lb   8 kg

j 25°C   25°F

k 2 lb   1 kg

l $\frac{2}{3}$ $\frac{7}{10}$

D2 Copy and complete the following conversions as accurately as you can using the scales on the opposite page.

a 5 kg =   lb   **b** 16 lb =   kg   **c** 100°F =   °C

d 30°C =   °F   **e** 0.75 =   **f** $\frac{1}{4}$ =

g 9 kg =   lb   **h** 9 lb =   kg   **i** 3°C =   °F

j 3°F =   °C   **k** $\frac{1}{3}$ =   **l** 0.67 =

Information given by scales can also be written as a conversion table:

Temperature	
°F	°C
0	−17.8
10	−12.2
20	−6.7
30	−1.1
40	4.4
50	10.0
60	15.6
70	21.1
80	26.7
90	32.2
100	37.8
110	43.3
120	48.9
130	54.4
140	60.0
150	65.6
160	71.1
170	76.7
180	82.2
190	87.8
200	93.4
210	98.9

A hot summer's day in England

Use the temperature conversion table above to answer the following questions as accurately as you can:

D3 Body temperature is 36.8°C. What is this in °F?

D4 Water freezes at 0°C. What is this in °F?

D5 Room temperature is 22°C. What is this in °F?

D6 At what temperature does water boil? Give both °C and °F.

D7 What do you think the temperature is in °C on a hot summer's day in England?

E Cable networks

Cable Television Ltd is planning to introduce cable TV to several areas. One of their problems is to plan a route for the cable which will use the minimum amount of cable.

The dots in the following diagrams represent towns, the numbers are the distances between the towns in kilometres.

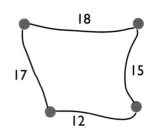

It is not necessary to join every town to every other town, as long as all the towns are linked into the cable network.

As the network gets bigger, a strategy is needed. A possible rule for adding a new town is to connect it to the nearest town already on the network.

Look at this diagram for five towns P–T:

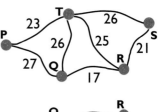

Step 1: Start with the shortest link QR.

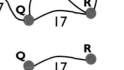

Step 2: The nearest town to the link QR is S.

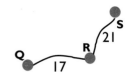

Step 3: The next nearest town on the network linking QR and RS is T.

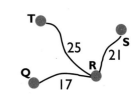

Step 4: Finally, the last town P is connected to its nearest town on the network, which is T.

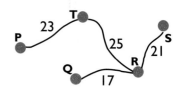

E1   Use the above method to find the shortest network to connect these six towns.

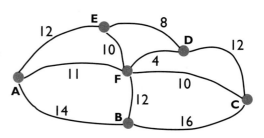

E2   Use a ruler to measure the distances between the cities on the map and put them on a rough diagram.

E3   Use the strategy just described on the opposite page to link up these cities. Calculate the shortest amount of cable needed.

E4   If Birmingham was chosen as the starting point of the cable network, would the amount of cable needed be different from your answer to question **E3**?

UNIT 7 *Listing possibilities*

A Possibility space

Sanji and Fred have arrived at
The Adventure Club camp
for a week's holiday.

They have been asked to pick
two activities for the next day,
one to do in the morning and
one in the afternoon.

A1 List all their possible choices, using the first letter of each activity. For
example, the choice of Pony Trekking and Canoeing becomes P C.
So their list might start   P C

                                     P A

                                     P R

                                     P O   etc.

A tidier way of displaying their choices is in a table like the following,
which is called a **possibility space**.

Morning activity

	Pony trekking (P)	Canoeing (C)	Abseiling (A)	Rock climbing (R)	Orienteering (O)
Pony trekking (P)	P P	C P	A P	R P	O P
Canoeing (C)	P C	C C			
Abseiling (A)					
Rock climbing (R)					
Orienteering (O)					

**Afternoon
activity**

A2 Copy and complete the table above.

A3 **a** In how many ways can Sanji and Fred do the same activity in the
morning and afternoon?

    b If they want to do canoeing and do not mind what the other activity
is, how many different possibilities are there?

    c What is the probability of doing a Rock climbing session on the first
day? (Hint: number of choices including R ÷ total number of choices).

Using possibility spaces as a display

A4 **a** Sanji goes to the camp tuck shop twice and buys one item each time. The tuck shop sells crisps, chocolate bars, biscuits, apples, peanuts and sweets. What choices can he make? List them.

b How many choices include peanuts?

c Sanji is given a lunch pack. He dislikes apples. If two of the above items are included at random (with equal probability) in a lunch pack, what is the probability that Sanji gets an apple? (Hint: how many choices include an apple? How many choices are there altogether?)

A5 Fred has two accidents, one in the morning and one in the afternoon. For that day, the accident book logs a broken arm, a twisted ankle, a bruised knee, a cut finger and a friction burn.

a What possible combination of accidents could Fred have had?

b What is the probability that Fred broke his arm
i in the morning **ii** in the afternoon?

A6 On the last day of their holiday, there is a competition. In the final round, five boys and girls, including Sanji and Fred, take part. Three points are allotted for coming first, two for coming second, one for coming third.

a List the possible positions that Sanji and Fred could achieve in the competition.

b In how many of these possibilities do Sanji and Fred together score three or more points?

B Tree diagrams

Tree diagrams are drawn to illustrate events.

If an event has two possible outcomes, the tree diagram has two branches.

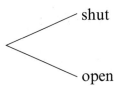

If an event has three possible outcomes, there are three branches.

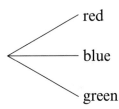

If a second event follows, it is drawn from the end of the first to show all possible combinations. For example, when going to the shops twice, the possibilities are as follows.

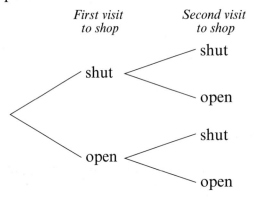

As the number of events increases, so the branches of the tree diagram grow:

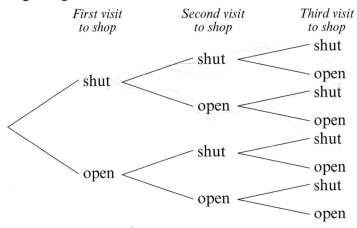

Families

In a family with one child, the child could be either a boy or a girl.

In a family with two children, the children could be:

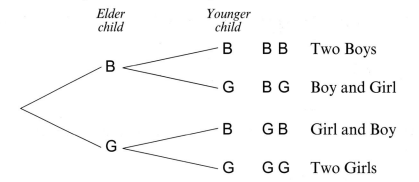

B1   In a family with three children, the children could be:

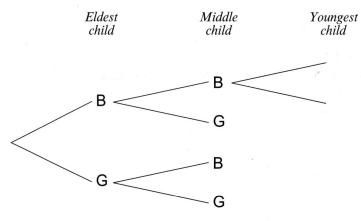

Copy and complete this tree diagram.

B2   Copy and complete this tree diagram for a family of four children.

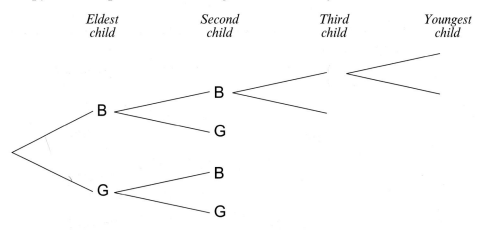

The information in a tree diagram can also be shown as a table.

B3   Using your tree diagrams from the previous page, copy and complete the following statements and tables:

One child

Number of different families containing one child

1 Boy	1 Girl
1	1

Two children
The possible combinations are: (GG), (GB, BG), (BB) with numbers 1, 2, 1.
The total number of possible combinations is 4.

Number of different families containing two children

2 Girls	1 Girl, 1 Boy	2 Boys
1	2	1

Three children
The possible combinations are: ...
The total number of possible combinations is ...

Number of different families containing three children

3 Girls	2 Girls, 1 Boy	1 Girl, 2 Boys	3 Boys

Four children
The possible combinations are: ...
The total number of possible combinations is ...

Number of different families containing four children

4 Girls	3 Girls, 1 Boy	2 Girls, 2 Boys	1 Girl, 3 Boys	4 Boys

The numbers required to complete the above tables form a pattern. This arrangement for combinations is known in the West as **Pascal's Triangle**. In fact, in China, it was partially known in the seventh century and well known by about 1100, long before the French mathematician Blaise Pascal was born in 1623.

B4   Copy and complete up to line 8.

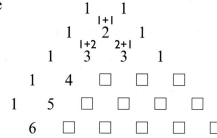

B5 Use the numbers from the Pascal Triangle completed in question **B4** to copy and complete the following tables:

a For *five* children

Number of ways to get families with five children

5 Girls	4 Girls, 1 Boy	3 Girls, 2 Boys	2 Girls, 3 Boys	1 Girl, 4 Boys	5 Boys

b For *six* children

Number of ways to get families with six children

6 Girls	5 Girls, 1 Boy	4 Girls, 2 Boys	3 Girls, 3 Boys	2 Girls, 4 Boys	1 Girl, 5 Boys	6 Boys

c List the possibilities for the outcome 5G, 1B.

Assuming that boys and girls are equally likely, it is possible to calculate the **probabilities** for each arrangement.

$$\text{The probability of an event} = \frac{\text{Number of times it happens}}{\text{Total number of events}}$$

Using the tables on page 65, the probability of each combination can be written in as shown here in red:

For *one* child

Number of different ways to get families with

1 Boy	1 Girl
1 $\frac{1}{2}$	1 $\frac{1}{2}$

For *two* children

Number of different ways to get families with

2 Girls	1 Girl, 1 Boy	2 Boys
1 $\frac{1}{4}$	2 $\frac{1}{4}+\frac{1}{4}=\frac{1}{2}$	1 $\frac{1}{4}$

B6 Copy and complete the table for

Three children

Number of different ways to get families with

3 Girls	2 Girls, 1 Boy	1 Girl, 2 Boys	3 Boys
1 $\frac{1}{8}$	3		

C Tossing a coin

When a coin is tossed,
it can land either head
or tail up.

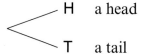

H   a head

T   a tail

If the coin is tossed again, the possible results are:

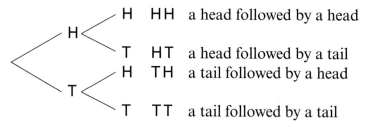

H   HH   a head followed by a head

T   HT   a head followed by a tail

H   TH   a tail followed by a head

T   TT   a tail followed by a tail

If the coin is tossed a third time, the possible results are:

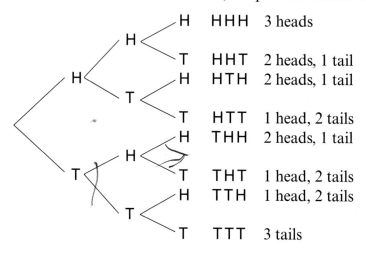

H   HHH   3 heads

T   HHT   2 heads, 1 tail

H   HTH   2 heads, 1 tail

T   HTT   1 head, 2 tails

H   THH   2 heads, 1 tail

T   THT   1 head, 2 tails

H   TTH   1 head, 2 tails

T   TTT   3 tails

C1 **a** Draw a table to show the frequency of each combination of heads
and tails if a coin is tossed two, three, four, five and six times.

 b Note any patterns.

 c Discuss these with another pupil.

D Rolling two dice

You will need two ordinary dice,
preferably of different colours.

2 dice

D1 Decide which of the two dice is to be recorded first. Place the two dice
side-by-side, with one facing upwards.
Prepare a diagram like the one below.
Keep the first dice at 1, change the second dice from 1 to 2, etc. and write
down the total score each time in the table.
Then change the first dice to 2, 3, etc. until you have recorded all the
possibilities.

First dice	Second dice	Total score
1	1	2
	2	3
	3	4
	4	5
	5	6
	6	7
2	1	3

D2 Copy this table and complete it using the diagram in question **D1**.

Scores

	2	3	4	5	6	7	8	9	10	11	12
Frequency											

D3 Use a different colour pen to write in on your table the probability of
each score happening. Remember that there are 36 possibilities. Total all
the probabilities and note any patterns.

E Other diagrams

There are occasions when tree diagrams or probability spaces are not a practical way of working out possibilities.

When a group of five people meet each other for the first time, everyone shakes hands with everyone else. How many hand-shakes will take place?

shakes with   shakes with   shakes with   shakes with

A —— B   B ⤜ A̶ already done   C ⤜ A̶ already done   D ⤜ A̶ already done
  ╲ C   ╲ B   B̶ already done   B̶ already done
  ╲ D   ╲ C   ╲ D   C̶ already done
  ╲ E   ╲ E   E   ╲ E

4   +   3   +   2   +   1   =   10 shakes

E1 Use this pattern to decide how many hand-shakes will take place when twenty people meet for the first time.

E2 Five company representatives meet at a conference. When the conference is over, each representative gives every other representative a business card.

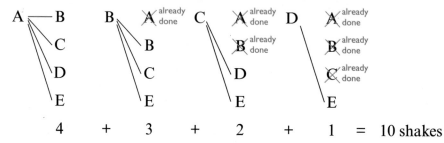

A will give one to { B   B will give one to { A
                       C   C
                       D   D
                       E   E   etc.

How many cards will be given out altogether?

Draw suitable diagrams, of your own choice, to illustrate questions **E3** to **E6**.

E3 In the football World Cup, the teams are divided into six sections. Teams are picked at random to become members of one section. In each section, the teams play each other once. The top two teams in each section move on to the next round.

   a If 36 teams start, how many games are needed to reduce the number to 12?

   b Devise a way of reducing the 12 teams to 4 teams for the semi-finals.

E4 Twenty people enter a tennis tournament. Design three ways to decide a winner. Which type of tournament takes the least number of matches?

E5 Eighteen athletes enter for a race. There are eight lanes on the track. Devise a suitable set of races, to determine a winner, which keeps everyone's chances of winning to a maximum.

E6 In a multiple-choice test, four possible answers are supplied for each question. Only one of the answers is correct. Mary knows very little about the subject of the test, so she decides to choose an answer completely at random for each question. What is the chance that she will guess five correct answers out of five?

UNIT 8 *It all adds up to 1*

A Everyday probabilities

A1 The number of days a particular bus arrives on time is 3 in a week of 7 days. The number of times that you arrive at the bus-stop on time is 2 days in the week.
(Remember: the probability of an event happening is the number of times it happens divided by the number of times it could happen.)

  a What is the probability that the bus arrives on time?

  b What is the probability that the bus arrives late?

  c Add the last two probabilities together. Explain the result.

  d What is the probability that you will arrive at the bus stop on time?

  e What is the probability that you arrive late?

  f Add the last two probabilities together.
  Explain why the answer must be 1.

A2 Five hundred raffle tickets are sold. There are ten prizes. The probability that you buy a ticket is one tenth.

  a What is the probability of winning a prize?

  b What is the probability of not winning a prize?

  c Add the last two answers together. Explain the result.

  d Give two different ways of working out the answer to part b.

  e What is the probability that you do not buy a raffle ticket?

A3 In November it rains, on average three days each week. Steve gets a lift to work on three days a week but has to cycle on the other two days.

  a On a working week-day chosen at random, what is the probability that Steve gets a lift to work?

  b What is the probability that Steve does not get a lift to work on that day?

  c Add the answers to parts a and b together. Explain the result.

  d What is the probability that it rains on a November day?

  e What is the probability that it does not rain on a November day?

  f Describe two ways of working out the probability that it does not rain.

Tree diagrams can be used to illustrate the three examples opposite.

The notation P(...) is short-hand for the probability of the event, written in brackets, occurring.

A4 Copy and complete:

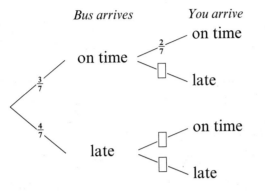

P(both on time) $= \frac{3}{7} \times \frac{2}{7} =$ ___

P(bus on time, $= \frac{3}{7} \times \frac{5}{7} =$ ___
you late)

P(_____) $=$ _____ $=$ ___

P(_____) $=$ _____

Total $=$ ___

A5 Copy and complete:

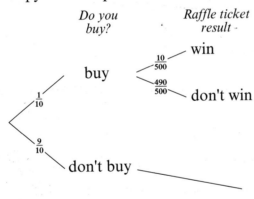

P(buy and win) $= \frac{1}{10} \times \frac{10}{500} = \frac{10}{5000}$

P(__ and __) $= \frac{1}{10} \times \frac{490}{500} = \frac{490}{5000}$

P(_____) $=$ _____ $=$ ___

Total $=$ ___

A6 Copy and complete:

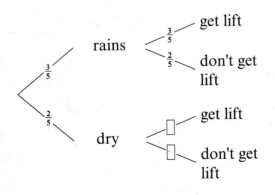

P(rains and $= \frac{3}{5} \times \frac{3}{5} = \frac{9}{25}$
get lift)

P(_____) $=$ _____ $=$ ___

P(_____) $=$ _____ $=$ ___

P(_____) $=$ _____ $=$ ___

Total $=$ ___

B More probabilities

B1 One day a week, Paula eats school lunch.
Two days a week she goes to lunch-time activities.

    a What is the probability that she eats school lunch?

    b What is the probability that she does not eat school lunch?

    c To what question does $(1 - \frac{4}{5})$ give you the answer?

    d What is the probability that Paula goes to lunch-time activities?

    e What is the probability that Paula does not go to lunch-time activities?

    f What is the total of the last two answers? What does it mean?

B2 The postman delivers letters to your door on average four days a week out of six. There is post for you on a quarter of the days he delivers.

    a What is the probability that on any particular day the postman delivers to your door? Call this P(delivers letters).

    b What is the probability that on any particular day the postman does not deliver anything?

    c What does '1 – P(deliver letters)' mean?

    d What is this probability?

B3 Two days a week, Mohammed forgets his calculator. He has mathematics lessons at school on three days a week out of five.

    a What is the probability that he remembers his calculator on a particular day?

    b How did you work out your answer to part a? Give another way.

    c What is the likelihood that, on any particular day, Mohammed has mathematics?

    d What is the likelihood that, on any particular day, Mohammed does not have mathematics?

    e Why do the last two answers add up to 1?

Tree diagrams can again be used to illustrate the examples on page 73.

B4   Copy and complete:

Has school   *Attends*
lunch   *activity*

                              yes   P(_____) =

        yes

                              no   P(_____) =

                              yes   P(_____) =

        no

                              no   P(_____) =

                                                    Total = ___

B5   Copy and complete:

Postman   *Has letter*
calls   *for you*

                              yes   P(calls and has = _____
                $\frac{1}{4}$ letter for you)
        yes
                $\frac{3}{4}$ P(_____) = _____
                              no

        $\frac{4}{6}$

        ☐

                no ——————— ?

                                                    Total = ___

B6   Look again at question **B3**. Design your own tree diagram for Mohammed.

C **Venn diagrams**

Venn diagrams are named after a nineteenth-century English logician, John Venn (1834–1883). He devised a system using circles (or loops) inside a rectangle to show how different groups can be connected within a population.

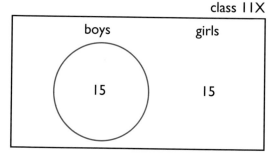

class 11X

For example, in class 11X there are 30 boys and girls. They are represented as being within a rectangle.

Inside the rectangle, the 15 boys in the class are represented as being within a circle. The 15 girls are within the rectangle but outside the circle.

Here is a Venn diagram for class 11Z.

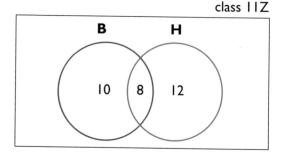

class 11Z

The number of boys in 11Z is represented inside the blue circle labelled B.

The pupils who play hockey are represented by the red circle labelled H.

C1 What do these areas represent in the diagram above? Be sure to say if they are boys or girls and whether they play hockey.

a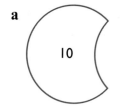

b

c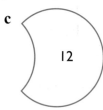

d   What is the probability that a pupil chosen at random will play hockey?

e   What is the probability that a pupil chosen at random will be a boy?

f   What is the probability that a pupil chosen at random will be a boy who plays hockey?

g   What is the probability that a pupil chosen at random will be a girl who plays hockey?

h   Which two probabilities total 1? Explain.

C2   This Venn diagram considers pupils in class 10P, all of whom study music or art or both.

Inside the red circle is the number of pupils who study music.
Inside the blue circle is the number of pupils who study art.

a   What does the section where the two circles overlap represent?

b   How many pupils study art?

c   What is the probability that a pupil chosen at random is studying art?

d   How many pupils study music?

e   What is the probability that a pupil chosen at random is studying music?

f   How many pupils study both music and art?

g   What is the probability that a pupil chosen at random is studying both music and art?

h   Add up the answers to parts **c**, **e** and **g**. Why does it *not* total 1?

C3 This Venn diagram shows the number of girls who compete for their school at swimming, hockey and/or netball:

The circle S contains the swimmers, the circle H contains the hockey players and the circle N contains the netball players.

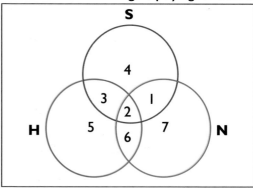

girls playing for school

Look at the parts of the Venn diagram below. Write down what each part means. For example:

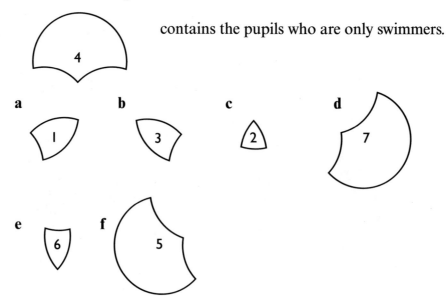

contains the pupils who are only swimmers.

a   1
b   3
c   2
d   7

e   6
f   5

Draw Venn diagrams for each of the situations described in questions **C4** to **C7**.

C4 Twenty-five business managers go to a conference in Switzerland. Three speak French and German. One speaks German only. Twelve speak French only.

a   How many speak neither French nor German?

b   If one of the business managers is chosen at random, what is
   i P(French speaking) **ii** P(German speaking) **iii** P(speaks neither)?

C5 Forty farms in the Lake District keep either sheep or cattle or both. Twenty-five of them keep cattle and twenty keep sheep.

    a How many keep both cattle and sheep?

    b If a farm is chosen at random, what is
      i P(keeps cattle and sheep)   **ii** P(keeps sheep)   **iii** P(keeps cattle)?

C6 Thirty households on a housing estate own cars. Eight houses have both a British and a foreign car. Twelve have a British car only. Ten have a foreign car only.
What is the probability that a family chosen at random will own

    a a British and a foreign car

    b a foreign car?

C7

The Wilson household consists of eight people, five of whom will only eat brown bread. Three will eat either white or brown bread.

    a How many will eat only white bread?

    b What is the probability that one of them chosen at random will eat only white bread?

    c What is the probability that one of them chosen at random will eat only brown bread?

D Miscellaneous situations

D1

The pupils of class 11T are weighed.
Their weights in kilograms are as follows:

61.9 61.7 68.1 67.6 67.0 75.5 66.2 65.9 65.3 64.8

68.7 69.4 74.1 73.1 72.3 71.8 71.3 70.1 69.2 68.8

61.4 69.4 67.2 70.3 66.1 73.5 65.8 75.2 63.4 62.9

a Copy and complete the table below. In the last column, put the
probability that a pupil chosen at random will be in the group.

Weight	Tally	Frequency	Probability
61.0–64.9 65.0–68.9 69.0–72.9 73.0–76.9			
Total		

b To which weight group is a pupil chosen at random most likely
to belong?

D2 A class of pupils were asked to estimate the length of a line in
centimetres. Their estimates, in centimetres, are given below:

13.1 12.7 12.6 14.3 11.4 11.8 16.5 11.6 13.2 13.9 10.3 11.4

12.7   9.6 12.5 13.8 14.2 10.3   9.4 15.6 11.8 12.5 10.7 11.6

Construct a table like the one in question **D1**.
State which range of lengths the class was most likely to choose.

D3 The pie chart shows how pupils get to school.

   a What is the probability that a pupil chosen at random goes by car?

   b What is the probability that the pupil does not go by car?

   c What is the probability that the pupil does not cycle?

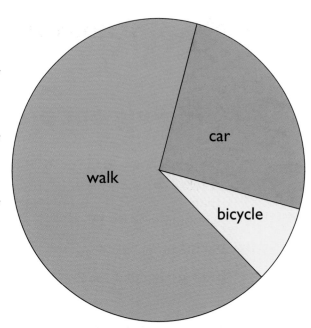

D4 This chart also shows how pupils get to school.

   a What is the probabilty that a pupil chosen at random walks to school?

   b What is the probability that the pupil does not walk?

   c What is the probability that the pupil travels by bus?

   d What is the probability that the pupil does not travel by car?

Bus

Car

Cycle

Walk

Key: each complete symbol represents 10 pupils

D5 The table shows the results for a group of people who took a driving test.

   a What is the probabilty of a man in the group chosen at random passing the test?

   b What is the probabilty of a man chosen at random failing the test?

	Pass	Fail	Total
Men	18	12	
Women	15	15	
Total			

   c What is the probability of a person chosen at random being male?

   d What is the probability of a person chosen at random being female?

UNIT 9 *Theoretical calculations*

A Working out probabilities

If a coin is tossed, the probability of getting a head is $\frac{1}{2}$.
If two coins are tossed, the probability of getting two heads is less than $\frac{1}{2}$ since (H)(H) is only one of four equally likely possible combinations (H)(H), (H)(T), (T)(H), (T)(T)

So the probability of getting (H)(H) is $\frac{1}{2} \times \frac{1}{2} = \frac{1}{4}$, that is:

(Probability that the first coin is a head) ×
                         (Probability that the second coin is a head).

A1 If three coins are tossed, what is the probability of getting three heads?

A slightly different calculation is needed to find the probability that the coins will come down all the same.

If four coins are tossed, the coins will come down all the same in two ways:

$$\text{(H)(H)(H)(H) or (T)(T)(T)(T)}$$

$$P(\text{(H)(H)(H)(H)}) = \frac{1}{2} \times \frac{1}{2} \times \frac{1}{2} \times \frac{1}{2} = \frac{1}{16}$$

$$\text{and} \quad P(\text{(T)(T)(T)(T)}) = \frac{1}{2} \times \frac{1}{2} \times \frac{1}{2} \times \frac{1}{2} = \frac{1}{16}$$

As there are *two* possible answers, we **add** the probabilities:

$$P(\text{(H)(H)(H)(H)}) + P(\text{(T)(T)(T)(T)}) = \frac{1}{16} + \frac{1}{16} = \frac{2}{16} = \frac{1}{8}$$

That is, there is a 1 in 8 chance of obtaining 4 heads or 4 tails when 4 coins are tossed.

On the next page, there are some questions using coins and dice for you to answer.

A2   **a**   If two fair (unbiased) coins are tossed, what is the probability of getting two tails?

    b   A biased coin, with a probability of a head = $\frac{1}{3}$, is tossed twice.

      i   What is the probability of two heads?

      ii   What is the probability of not having two heads?

      iii   What is the probability of two heads if the same coin is tossed three times?

A3   Here are some unusual fair dice.

    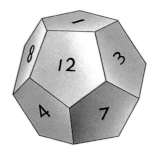

Tetrahedral dice
4 similar faces
numbered 1 to 4

Octahedral dice
8 similar faces
numbered 1 to 8

Dodecahedral dice
12 similar faces
numbered 1 to 12

  For each of the dice above:

    a   What is the probability of   **i**   getting a 4?

                                 ii   not getting a 4?

    b   What is the probability of   **i**   getting a number less than 3?

                                 ii   getting a number greater than 3?

A4   What is the most likely score if two tetrahedral dice are thrown and the scores are added?

A5   What are the chances of getting two scores the same if two octahedral dice are thrown?

B **Fruit machines**

Fruit machines have three windows showing pictures of fruit. The machines pay out either tokens or money when the three pictures are the same. For example, three oranges or three bananas.

Behind each window in a fruit machine is a barrel with pictures of fruit on it.

A strip of pictures of fruit, like the one on the right, is wrapped round each barrel.

Each barrel is *identical*. All three barrels spin when a lever is pulled. When the barrels stop spinning, each picture on the strip is equally likely to appear in each window.

So, for the first window, the chances of an orange are 2 out of 9 because there are only 2 oranges in the strip of 9 fruits.

B1   Work out the probability for each of the other fruits appearing in the first window.

As all the barrels are similar, the probabilities calculated for the first window are also true for the second and third windows.

B2   What is the probability of getting the following winning combinations
of fruits?

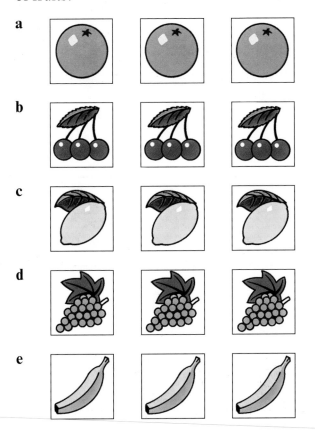

B3   Which combination in question B2 should pay out most? Explain why.

B4   If you could HOLD (stop) the first barrel from spinning and spin the
other two, like this:

What is the probability of getting a winning combination?

Extension work

B5   **a**   What is the total number of combinations for the three windows?

   b   How do you deal with the fact that some fruits have more chances of
appearing on each barrel?

   c   How many of the total number of combinations are winners?

   d   How does this fit in with your answer to question **B3**?

Fruit machines sometimes have different sets of fruits on each barrel.

The strips which go round the barrels may be like those shown on the right.

The winning combinations are as follows:

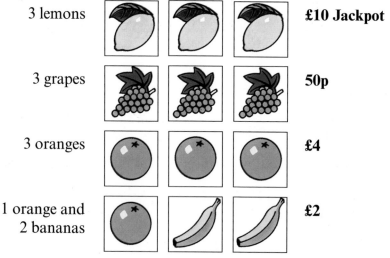

3 lemons			**£10 Jackpot**
3 grapes			**50p**
3 oranges			**£4**
1 orange and 2 bananas			**£2**

B6 What is the probability of getting:

    a the Jackpot   **b** each of the other winning lines?

B7 **a** Is the chance of winning 50p for 3 bunches of grapes 20 times the chance of winning the Jackpot?

    b Do the other prizes reflect the probability fairly?

B8 If you pay 20p a go and you have 216 goes,

    a what winnings may you expect

    b are you likely to make a profit

    c what changes would make the prizes more fair?

C Dominoes

A domino is made of two squares.
Dots are put on each square to
represent the numbers from
0 (blank) to 6.

This domino shows 2 4.

The table below shows all the possible combinations of numbers which
can be marked on dominoes:

00	10	20	30	40	50	60
01	11	21	31	41	51	61
02	12	22	32	42	52	62
03	13	23	33	43	53	63
04	14	24	34	44	54	64
05	15	25	35	45	55	65
06	16	26	36	46	56	66

Total $7 + 7 + 7 + 7 + 7 + 7 + 7 = 49$

C1   Make a copy of the table above.

Notice that there are some duplicates in the table of combinations of
numbers. A domino can be turned round so that 1 5 is the same as 5 1.

Some dominoes are 'doubles', such as 3 3. Are these duplicated?

On your copy, put a ring round each of the doubles. Then cross out all
the duplicates to the right of the line of doubles.

Did you cross out all of them on the right?

Now count the number of dominoes remaining which are not duplicated.

Did you get 28?

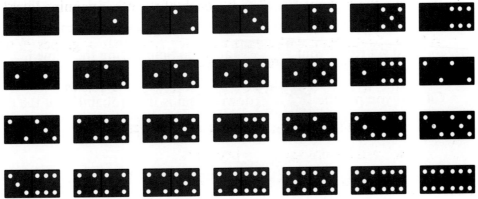

C2   **a**   How many dominoes have a 0 (or blank) on them?

       b   Is it the same number for the other numbers on the dominoes?

       c   What is the probability of choosing a domino with a 4 on it?

       d   Is it the same probability for other numbers?

Extension work

In the game of dominoes, two players each have a random selection of dominoes. The players play alternately and, if possible, add one of their dominoes to the line of dominoes between them. The added domino must match the one it touches. Doubles are often placed across the line. The object of the game is to get rid of all your dominoes before your opponent.

Here is a game which has started. [Note: The real game of dominoes uses more pieces than shown in the following questions. A simplified version poses similar probability questions to those found in the real game.]

Four dominoes have been placed in a line:

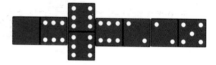

You have these six dominoes:

It is your turn to play.

You have to match either a blank or a 5, so you can put down one of these three dominoes:

C3   If you put down , what is the probability of a 5 turning up at either end of the line of dominoes next time? (Remember that you have to get rid of your at some time during the game.)

C4   If you put the down, what is the probability of the dominoes in the line allowing you to play your ?

C5   If you place your against the blank , what is the probability of your being able to use your remaining 4s?

In the following questions, explain which domino you would play and why.

C6 The dominoes on the table are:

You have six dominoes.

C7 The dominoes on the table are:

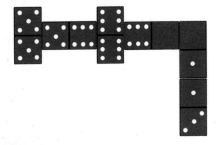

You have five dominoes.

C8 The dominoes on the table are:

You have seven dominoes.

D Miscellaneous Challenge

D1 Harry Jerriott, the local vet, has been called out to Mr Higginbotham's farm to treat foot rot in six of his sheep. Unfortunately, Mr Higginbotham's son left a gate open and the six infected sheep returned to the field to join the fourteen healthy sheep which were grazing there.

    a What is the probability that the first sheep in the field seen by the vet will have foot rot?

    b What is the probability that the last sheep seen by the vet will have foot rot? (Take care!)

D2 One in four of Mr Higginbotham's twenty sheep produce triplets at lambing time. The rest produce twins.

    a How many lambs will the twenty sheep produce?

    b One of each triplet needs to be reared by hand. How many lambs does Mr Higginbotham hand-rear?

D3 Mr Higginbotham also has twenty cows. Each cow produces a calf every year but one in five cows produces twins. How many calves can Mr Higginbotham expect each year?

D4 In a packet of fourteen biscuits, five are broken. What is the probability of choosing a broken biscuit?

D5 A different packet, containing seventeen biscuits, has seven which are broken. What is the probability of choosing two biscuits from this packet, both of which are broken?

D6 A packet of fruit gums contains three flavours: blackcurrant, raspberry and orange. They are packed in tubes of six, two of each flavour, in any order.

    a What is the probability of two orange gums being placed together?

    b What is the probability of two orange gums not being next to each other?

D7 Susan has made sixteen cups of coffee and put sugar in two of them. She has forgotten which two cups contain sugar. On the tray is a plate of biscuits with three chocolate and thirteen plain biscuits. She delivers, at random, a cup of coffee and a biscuit to all sixteen people in her office.

    a What is the probability that the first person gets:

       i a cup of coffee with sugar and a chocolate biscuit

       ii a cup of coffee without sugar and a chocolate biscuit

       iii a cup of coffee with sugar and a plain biscuit

       iv a cup of coffee without sugar and a plain biscuit?

    b Which combination are Susan's colleagues most likely to get?

    c Which combination are Susan's colleagues least likely to get?

Handling data 3
National Curriculum
level description coverage

NC level 6 description	Covered in pupils' Unit:
• collect and record continuous data, choosing appropriate equal class intervals over a sensible range to create frequency tables	1, 2, 3
• construct and interpret frequency diagrams	1, 2, 4, 6
• draw conclusions from scatter diagrams, and have a basic understanding of correlation	5
• identify all the outcomes using diagrammatic, tabular or other forms of communication, when dealing with a combination of two experiments	7, 9
• in solving problems, use the knowledge that the total probability of all mutually exclusive outcomes of an experiment is 1	8, 9
• using and applying the above skills	All Units

Important note

There are several parts of the book which cover content not stated explicitly in the National Curriculum at Level 6. The Level Descriptions are minimum statements which do not include all implied content.

In particular, Units 1, 2 and 3 include both discrete and continuous data together with some historical background. Units 4 and 6 together provide a wide range of exercises: teachers may need to be selective in choosing examples. Unit 9, which provides further challenges in probability, is partly revision.